Scott Foresman - Addison Wesley
MIDDLE SCHOOL MATH

Problem-Solving Workbook
For Guided Problem Solving

Course 2

Scott Foresman - Addison Wesley

Editorial Offices: Menlo Park, California • Glenview, Illinois
Sales Offices: Reading, Massachusetts • Atlanta, Georgia • Glenview, Illinois
Carrollton, Texas • Menlo Park, California

http://www.sf.aw.com

ISBN 0–201–31829-6

Printed in the United States of America

2 3 4 5 6 7 8 9 10 – BW – 02 01 00 99

Contents

Overview

The *Problem-Solving Workbook* (For Guided Problem Solving) provide a step-by-step approach to solve a problem selected from the student book. These selections are made from the *Practice and Apply* section or from the *Problem Solving and Reasoning* section. Some of these selections are routine in nature and cover basic concepts. Others are nonroutine and might involve multiple-step problems, problems with too much information, problems involving critical thinking, and so on. An icon in the Teacher's Edition flags the selected problem so that the teacher will know what problem is provided on each worksheet.

How to use

The Problem-Solving Worksheets are designed so that the teacher can use them in many different ways:

a. As a teaching tool to guide students in exploring and mastering a specific problem-solving skill or strategy. Making a transparency of the worksheet provides an excellent way to expedite this process as students work along with the teacher at their desks.

b. As additional practice in solving problems for students who have had difficulty in completing the assignment.

c. As independent or group work to help students reach a better understanding of the problem-solving process.

d. As a homework assignment that may encourage students to involve their parents in the educational process.

Description of the master

The problem to be solved is stated at the top of each worksheet. The worksheet is then divided into the four steps of the Problem-Solving Guidelines that are used throughout the student text. Each step includes key questions designed to guide students through the problem-solving process. At the bottom of each worksheet, *Solve Another Problem* allows students to use their skills to solve a problem similar to the original problem. This helps reinforce the problem-solving skills and strategies they have just used in solving the problem on the worksheet.

The Guided Problem Solving worksheet on the next page can be used as a guide to help students organize their work as they complete the *Solve Another Problem*. It may also be used to assist students in solving any problem as they complete the four steps of the Problem-Solving Guidelines.

1. **Understand** ensures that students are able to interpret the problem and determine key facts.

2. **Plan** actively involves students in devising a plan or strategy for solving the problem. They may be asked to choose a fact or formula that could be used to solve the problem. In other cases, students may be asked to model the problem or draw a picture. Other times, students will be asked to choose a strategy they can use to solve the problem. Problem-solving strategies often used include: Look for a Pattern, Make a Table, Work Backward, Draw a Diagram, Make an Organized List, Guess and Check, Use Logical Reasoning, and Solve a Simpler Problem.

3. **Solve** encourages students to carry out the plan and arrive at an answer. Students may be asked to answer the question using a full sentence.

4. **Look Back** encourages students to review their work and check their answer to see if it is reasonable. This step often asks students to reflect on the strategy they used or to suggest other strategies they could also have used to solve the problem. It is important that students think of this step as a natural part of the problem-solving process.

Name _____

GPS PROBLEM

━━ **Understand** ━━

━━ **Plan** ━━━━

━━ **Solve** ━━━━

━━ **Look Back** ━━

Name _____

 **PROBLEM 6, STUDENT PAGE 10**

The bar graph at the right is misleading. About how many times greater than the population of Seoul are the populations of Tokyo and Bombay?

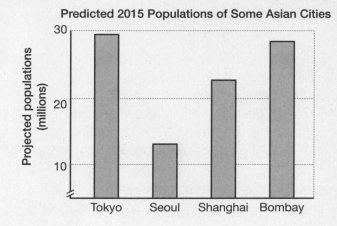

Predicted 2015 Populations of Some Asian Cities

Understand

1. Underline the question.

2. About how much taller is the bar for Tokyo than the one for Seoul?

   _____

3. Why is this misleading? _____

   _____

Plan

4. Estimate the population of Tokyo. _____

5. Estimate the population of Seoul. _____

6. Estimate the population of Bombay. _____

Solve

7. About how many times greater than the population of Seoul is the population of Tokyo? (Hint: Divide the estimated population of Tokyo by the estimated population of Seoul.) _____

8. About how many times greater than the population of Seoul is the population of Bombay? _____

Look Back

9. Look at your answers to Items 2 and 7. Explain how you would fix the graph so it is not misleading.

   _____

   _____

SOLVE ANOTHER PROBLEM

About how many times greater than the population of Seoul is the population of Shanghai? _____

Name _____

GPS **PROBLEM 11, STUDENT PAGE 15**

Look at the table showing Armando's salary for the years 1996–2000.

a. Would this data best be shown on a bar graph or a circle graph?

b. Make a graph of the data.

c. What do you notice about Armando's salary in the years 1996 to 1999?

d. What do you think happened to Armando in the year 2000?

Armando's Salary	
Year	Salary in dollars
1996	20,000
1997	23,000
1998	26,000
1999	29,000
2000	35,000

— Understand —

1. Will the graph show parts of a whole or different amounts? _____

— Plan —

2. Which of these scales would you choose for the vertical axis on the graph? _____

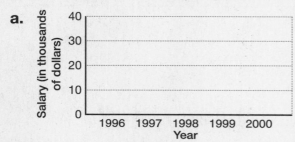

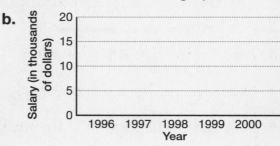

— Solve —

3. Draw your graph at the right.

4. Do the bars for 1996-1999 show a steady increase or decrease in Armando's salary?

_____

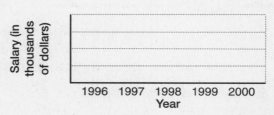

5. What might have happened in the year 2000? _____

_____

— Look Back —

6. Does your graph match the change in Armando's salary each year? _____

SOLVE ANOTHER PROBLEM

Suppose that Armando's salary in the year 2000 was $22,000. Describe how you would change the graph to reflect this information.

_____

Name _____

GPS PROBLEM 10, STUDENT PAGE 20

The back-to-back stem-and-leaf diagram shows the average daily April temperatures for Boston, MA, and Portland, OR. Use the plot to compare the pattern of April temperatures in the two cities.

Boston, MA		Portland, OR
	7	1
2 2	6	0 0 0 1 1 1 1 2 3 3 4 5
9 8 7 7 7 5 3 3 1 1 1 0	5	2 5 5 5 6 6 6 7 8 9 9
8 8 8 7 4 4 2 2 0 0	4	2 2 3 4 4 5
6 6 4 3 3 0	3	

Understand

1. What do the digits in the stem represent? _____

2. Which leaves, on the right or the left, show temperatures for each city?

   a. Portland _____   **b.** Boston _____

Plan

3. The lowest temperature for Boston was 30°. The highest temperature was 62°. For Portland, what was the

   a. lowest temperature? _____   **b.** highest temperature? _____

4. How many more days was the temperature in the 60s and 70s in Portland than in Boston? _____

Solve

5. Write a sentence comparing the temperature patterns for the two cities.

   _____

Look Back

6. How can you compare the pattern without comparing the actual temperatures?

   _____

   _____

   _____

SOLVE ANOTHER PROBLEM

The back-to-back stem-and-leaf diagram shows the number of minutes two teams practice each day. What pattern do you notice?

Team A		Team B
1	7	0 3 5 9
7	6	2 7 7
6 1	5	3 8
9 2 1	4	8
7 5 4	3	

_____

GPS PROBLEM 12, STUDENT PAGE 25

Six piglets in a litter had an average weight of 8 lb. Find two possibilities for the weight of each pig.

— Understand —

1. What is another term for "average weight"? _____

2. Which range do you think the piglets weight should fall within? _____

    a. 0–8 pounds   **b.** 3–13 pounds   **c.** 8–16 pounds

— Plan —

3. An average weight of 8 pounds for the six piglet means that: _____

    a. Each piglet weighs 8 pounds.
    b. The total weight of the piglets can be found by multiplying 6 and 8.

4. How much do the six piglets weigh in all? _____

— Solve —

5. Find a set of reasonable weights whose sum is equal to your answer in Item 4.

_____

6. Find another set of reasonable weights whose sum is equal to your answer in Item 4.

_____

— Look Back —

7. How can you check to see if your answer is reasonable?

_____

_____

SOLVE ANOTHER PROBLEM

Seven golden retriever puppies had an average weight of 12 lb. Find two possibilities for the weight of each dog.

_____

Name _____

GPS **PROBLEM 11, STUDENT PAGE 34**

The Carolina Panthers joined the NFL in 1995.
The double-line graph shows the number of
points scored and allowed by the Panthers
in the first nine games of their first season.
In how many games did the Panthers score
more points than their opponents?
How can you tell? How could you tell if
there was a tie game?

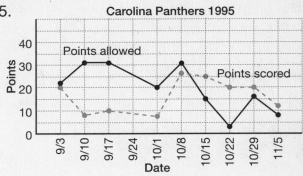

— Understand —

1. Look at the broken line to find how
   many points the Panthers scored on 9/3. _____

2. Look at the solid line to find how many points
   they allowed the opposing team to score on 9/3. _____

3. If the line for points scored is below the line
   for points allowed, did the Panthers win or lose? _____

— Plan —

4. How many times is the line for points
   scored above the line for points allowed. _____

— Solve —

5. In how many games did the Panthers score more points than their
   opponents? How can you tell?

   _____

   _____

6. Suppose both teams score 10 points. Describe what happens to the
   lines. Who wins the game?

   _____

— Look Back —

7. Write a number sentence to show that the Panther wins and the
   Panther losses equal the total games played.

   _____

| **SOLVE ANOTHER PROBLEM** |

In how many games did the Panthers score 10 or more points less than
their opponents? Give the dates of these games.

_____

Name _____

GPS **PROBLEM 13, STUDENT PAGE 39**

The scatterplot shows the number of cars crossing a toll bridge on the different days in May. Describe any patterns you see.

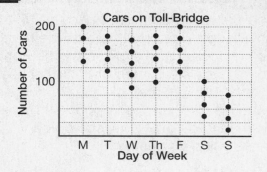

Cars on Toll-Bridge

━━ **Understand** ━━

1. Underline what you are asked to find.

2. Does the scatterplot show a positive, negative, or no relationship? What does this tell you about the trend? _____

━━ **Plan** ━━

3. On which day(s) were the number of cars between 100 and 200? Between 0 and 100?

_____

4. On which days does the number of cars seem to be about the same?

_____

━━ **Solve** ━━

5. What pattern do you notice in the scatterplot?

_____

━━ **Look Back** ━━

6. Is your answer to Item 5 reasonable? Explain.

_____

_____

SOLVE ANOTHER PROBLEM

The scatterplot shows the number of people that visited an amusement park on the different days of June. What do you think might account for any patterns that you see?

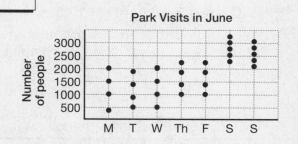

Park Visits in June

_____

_____

Name _____

GPS **PROBLEM 6, STUDENT PAGE 44**

The scatterplot shows the areas of some states and their 1996 population.

States: Areas and Populations

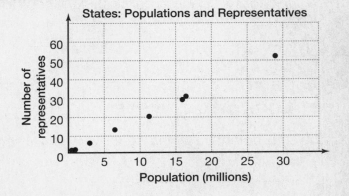

  a. Describe the scatterplot.
  b. Could you use the scatterplot to make any predictions?

━ Understand ━

1. Underline what you are asked to find.

━ Plan ━

2. Identify the relationship shown in the scatterplot. _____

    a. positive relationship   **b.** negative relationship   **c.** no relationship

3. Would a trend line help you make a prediction? Explain.

_____

━ Solve ━

4. Describe the scatterplot. Tell how area and population relate.

_____

5. Could you use the scatterplot to predict the population of a state with an area of 57,918 square miles? _____

━ Look Back ━

6. Does your answer make sense? Explain. _____

_____

| **SOLVE ANOTHER PROBLEM** |

The scatterplot shows the population of some states and the number of representatives from that state.

  a. Describe the scatterplot.

_____

_____

_____

States: Populations and Representatives

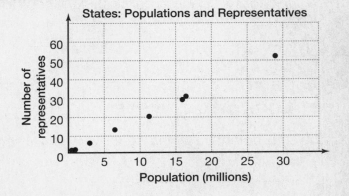

  b. Could you use the scatterplot to make any predictions? Explain.

_____

Name _____

GPS PROBLEM 14, STUDENT PAGE 59

You have to get your car stereo fixed. The repair shop charges $10 per hour, plus $30 for the visit. Use the formula $C = 10h + 30$, where C is cost and h is hours.

a. How much will it cost if the repairs take 3 hours?

b. Is this the same amount you would pay if you brought the stereo in once for 1 hour and once for 2 hours? Explain your reasoning.

Understand

1. Circle the information you need.

2. What value will you substitute for h in the formula if the repairs take

    a. 1 hour? _____   b. 2 hours? _____   c. 3 hours? _____

Plan

3. Make a table to organize the data.
   What will be the labels on the table? _____

Solve

4. Substitute values for h into the formula to complete the table.

5. How much will it cost if the repairs take 3 hours? _____

6. How much will it cost if the repairs take 1 hour during one service call and 2 hours during another service call? _____

7. Does it cost the same amount for a service call of 3 hours as it does for two service calls taking 1 hour and 2 hours? Explain.

_____

_____

Look Back

8. What other strategies could you have used to solve the problem?

_____

SOLVE ANOTHER PROBLEM

How much will it cost if the repairs take 6 hours? _____

GPS **PROBLEM 27, STUDENT PAGE 64**

The formula $C = p + ip$ gives the total cost (C) of an item where p is the cost of the item before tax and i is the tax rate.

a. What is the total cost of a $62 car battery if the tax rate is 5% (0.05)?

b. The formula $C = p(1 + i)$ will also give you the total cost. Use this formula to find the total cost of a $62.00 battery at the same tax rate.

c. How are the two formulas related?

▬ Understand ▬

1. Circle the information you need.

▬ Plan ▬

2. Which numbers will you substitute for p and i to find the cost of the $62 battery? _____

3. Which operation will you do first in order to solve

   a. $C = p + ip$? _____   **b.** $C = p(1 + i)$? _____

▬ Solve ▬

4. Use the formula $C = p + ip$ to find the total cost of a $62 car battery if the tax rate is 5% (0.05). _____

5. Use the formula $C = p(1 + i)$ to find the total cost of a $62.00 battery at the same rate. _____

6. The two formulas give the same answer, so $p + ip = p(1 + i)$. How do you know this is true and that the formulas are related?

_____

_____

▬ Look Back ▬

7. Which formula is easier to use? Explain.

_____

SOLVE ANOTHER PROBLEM

The formulas $A = s + t$ and $A = t + s$ give the area of the rectangle.

   a. What is the area of the rectangle if s is 10 and t is 5? . _____

   b. How are the formulas related? . _____

_____

GPS | **PROBLEM 3, STUDENT PAGE 69**

The Kelvin temperature scale is sometimes used in science. The formula $K = 273 + C$ relates degrees Kelvin (K) to degrees Celsius (C). Make a table that shows the Kelvin temperatures for the Celsius temperatures of 0°, 20°, 40°, 60°, 80°, and 100°.

— Understand —

1. Circle the data you need to make the table showing Kelvin and Celsius temperatures.

2. How do you use the formula to find degrees Kelvin?

_____

— Plan —

3. What labels will you use to show the two sets of information?

_____

4. Which data will go on the top row of your table? _____

— Solve —

5. Complete the table below, including labels.

— Look Back —

6. How can you use subtraction to check your answer?

_____

_____

SOLVE ANOTHER PROBLEM

The formula $C = \frac{5}{9}(F - 32)$ relates degrees Fahrenheit (F) to degrees Celsius (C). Make a table that shows the Celsius temperatures for the Fahrenheit temperatures of 50°, 68°, 77°, 95°, 104°, and 149°.

Name _____

GPS **PROBLEM 15, STUDENT PAGE 77**

A wolf had 10 pups in her third litter. The number of pups was twice as many as in her second litter, and her second litter had 3 more pups than her first. Find the number of pups in her first litter.

━━ Understand ━━

1. What is it you are asked to find?

_____

2. Has the number of pups been increasing or decreasing since her first litter? _____

3. How many litters has she had including her first? _____

━━ Plan ━━

4. The litter of 10 pups she just had was twice the number of pups in her second litter. How would you use this fact to find the number of pups in her second litter? _____

5. The number of pups in the wolf's second litter was 3 more than in her first litter. How would you use this fact to find the number of pups in her first litter, once you found the number of pups in her second litter? _____

━━ Solve ━━

6. Find the number of pups in her second litter. _____

7. Find the number of pups in her first litter. _____

━━ Look Back ━━

8. How can you check your answer?

_____

_____

SOLVE ANOTHER PROBLEM

There are 17 members in the three-year-old computer club. This is 2 more members than last year. Last year there were three times as many members as there were in the first year. How many members were in the computer club the first year? _____

Name _____

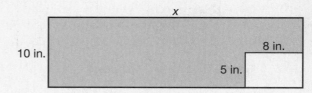

 PROBLEM 30, STUDENT PAGE 81

The area of a rectangle is equal to its length times its width. Write an algebraic expression to describe the area of the shaded portion of the large rectangle. Explain your reasoning.

Understand

1. What are the dimensions of the large rectangle?

_____

2. What are the dimensions of the small rectangle?

_____

Plan

3. Will the shaded area be larger or smaller than the area of the large rectangle? _____

4. What is the relationship between the areas of the large rectangle, the small rectangle, and the shaded area?

_____

_____

Solve

5. Write an expression for the area of the large rectangle. _____

6. Find the area of the small rectangle. _____

7. Write an algebraic expression to describe the area of the shaded portion of the large rectangle. _____

Look Back

8. How can you check your answer?

_____

_____

_____

SOLVE ANOTHER PROBLEM

Write an algebraic expression for the area of a sheet of paper 12 in. by 9 in. with a rectangle 4 in. by x in. cut out of its center. _____

Name _____

GPS PROBLEM 39, STUDENT PAGE 85

Igor Sikorsky built and flew the first practical helicopter in 1939, making it possible for vertical landing and takeoff in remote places. A helicopter was flying at 1300 feet, landed to pick up a load, and then took off. If the loaded helicopter flew at a height 115 feet lower than before, write and solve an equation to find the new height (h).

━━ Understand ━━

1. Underline what you are asked to do.

2. Circle the information you need.

3. Is 1300 feet more or less than the new height (h)? _____

━━ Plan ━━

4. How much would you need to add to the new height to get to 1300 feet? _____

5. Which is a reasonable solution? _____

   a. 1200 ft   **b.** 1800 ft   **c.** 1400 ft

━━ Solve ━━

6. Write an equation to show the information. _____

7. What will you need to do to both sides of your equation to find the solution? _____

8. Solve your equation. Show your work. _____

━━ Look Back ━━

9. Draw a picture to show that your answer makes sense.

SOLVE ANOTHER PROBLEM

The technology center has 25 computers, 28 monitors and 37 keyboards. If the number of monitors they have now is 7 more than the number they had last year (n), write and solve an equation to find how many monitors they had last year.

_____

GPS **PROBLEM 31, STUDENT PAGE 90**

Fingernails grow about 1.5 inches per year. The world record for the longest fingernails is 37 inches. Which equation shows how long it might take to grow nails 37 inches long?

(A) $1.5 + y = 37$ **(B)** $\frac{y}{1.5} = 37$ **(C)** $1.5y = 37$ **(D)** $y = 1.5 \times 37$

—— Understand ——

1. Circle what you are asked to find.
2. What does y represent in the equations? _____

—— Plan ——

3. What operation can you use to find the answer? _____

4. Explain how your answer to Item 3 would
allow you to eliminate some of the equations. _____

_____

—— Solve ——

5. Which equation would show that the total growth was 37 inches? _____

—— Look Back ——

6. Solve the equation. Why is your answer to Item 5 reasonable?

_____

_____

_____

| **SOLVE ANOTHER PROBLEM** |

There were 920 statistics textbooks ordered this year. This was 2.3 times the number that were ordered five years ago. Which equation shows how many statistics textbooks were ordered five years ago? Explain.

(A) $920 = s + 2.3$ **(B)** $\frac{s}{2.3} = 920$ **(C)** $920 - 2.3 = s$ **(D)** $2.3s = 920$

_____

_____

_____

Name _____

GPS | PROBLEM 21, STUDENT PAGE 93

Marco is making a mobile like the one in the diagram. Write an equation to show the mobile balanced. What should each of the small boxes weigh?

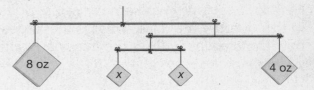

■ Understand ■

1. What is the total weight of the boxes on each side of the mobile? Explain how you know.

   _____

   _____

2. Since the two small boxes are both labeled x, can their weights be different? Explain.

   _____

   _____

■ Plan ■

3. What number will stand alone on one side of the equation? _____

4. How many x variables will you have in your equation? _____

■ Solve ■

5. Write an equation to show that the mobile is balanced. _____

6. What operation will you need to undo first? _____

7. What operation will you need to undo second? _____

8. Solve your equation. What will each of the small boxes weigh? _____

■ Look Back ■

9. How can you check to see if your answer is reasonable? _____

   _____

SOLVE ANOTHER PROBLEM

An adult that weighs 175 lb balances four children on a seesaw. One child weighs 70 lb. The other children weigh the same amount. Write and solve an equation to find the weight of the other children.

_____

Name _____

GPS ┃ **PROBLEM 20, STUDENT PAGE 109**

Here is a decimal with some missing digits: ☐3.☐8☐. If no two digits
of this number are alike, what is the largest possible number this can
be? The smallest? Fill in the missing digits to make the closest
possible number to $53\frac{1}{2}$.

━ Understand ━

1. Can you use a digit more than once? _____

2. What number must be in the tens place? The hundredths place? _____

━ Plan ━

3. Which digits can you use to make the decimals? _____

4. Which three digits will you use to make the largest
   possible number? The smallest possible number? _____

5. To find the number closest to $53\frac{1}{2}$, rewrite
   $53\frac{1}{2}$ as 53.500. Write 5 in the tens place.
   Decide which of the remaining digits make
   the decimal closest to 0.500.

$$5 \quad 3 \quad . \quad 5 \quad 0 \quad 0$$
$$\boxed{}\; 3 \;.\; \boxed{} \; 8 \; \boxed{}$$

━ Solve ━

6. Write the greatest possible number. _____

7. Write the least possible number. _____

8. What number is closest to $53\frac{1}{2}$? _____

━ Look Back ━

9. Why do you think your answer to Item 8 is reasonable?

_____

_____

┃ **SOLVE ANOTHER PROBLEM**

Here is a decimal with some missing digits: ☐4.☐8☐. If no two digits
of this number are alike, what is the largest possible number this can
be? The smallest? Fill in the missing digits to make the closest
possible number to $34\frac{1}{2}$.

_____

Name _____

 PROBLEM 38, STUDENT PAGE 113

A social service agency finds that on the average, 2.87 of every 100 families need help from the agency. About how many families can they expect to help in a town of 966 families?

━━ Understand ━━

1. What are you asked to find?

_____

_____

2. Do you need to find an exact answer or an estimate? _____

━━ Plan ━━

3. Use compatible numbers to estimate about how many 100s there are in 966. Write an equation.

_____

4. What number sentence shows about how many can be helped? _____

   a. 10 × 3000   **b.** 1000 × 10   **c.** 10 × 3

━━ Solve ━━

5. About how many families can the agency help? _____

━━ Look Back ━━

6. What strategy can you use to check your answer? Show an example.

_____

_____

_____

_____

_____
| **SOLVE ANOTHER PROBLEM** |

In the seventh grade at Howard Middle School, 2.14 out of every 100 students play the trumpet. There are 400 seventh graders at Howard. About how many students play trumpet?

_____

Name _____

GPS PROBLEM 25, STUDENT PAGE 119

Planetary probes have small engines that technicians on Earth can use to correct the path of a probe while it is traveling between planets. A probe to Jupiter started with 55.7 kg of fuel for its engine. The engine has been used three times. Use the table to calculate how much fuel has been used and how much is remaining.

Engine Firing	1	2	3
Fuel Used (kg)	12.87	9.3	11.22

■ Understand ■

1. How much fuel did the probe start with? _____

2. How many times has the engine been fired? _____

■ Plan ■

3. Write an expression that shows how much fuel the probe has used during the trip? _____

4. How much fuel has the probe used? _____

5. What operation will you use to find how much fuel is left? _____

■ Solve ■

6. Write a sentence that tells how much fuel the probe has left?

_____

_____

■ Look Back ■

7. Could you have found the amount of fuel remaining after the three trips by finding the fuel left after each trip? Explain.

_____

_____

| SOLVE ANOTHER PROBLEM |

How much fuel has been used and how much is remaining after two firings? _____

Name _____

GPS PROBLEM 34, STUDENT PAGE 124

As part of her research in astronomy, Nava has been calculating the speed of travel of the moons in the solar system. Here is some of the data she has collected for some of the moons of Jupiter. Complete the table.

Moon	Io	Ganymede	Callisto
Orbital Radius (km × 1,000,000)	0.42		
Period (days)	1.77	7.15	16.69
Orbital Distance (radius × 6.28)		6.7196	11.8064
Speed ($\frac{distance}{period}$)		0.94	

▬ Understand ▬

1. What formula is used to find the orbital distance? _____

2. What formula is used to find the speed? _____

▬ Plan ▬

3. Write an expression for finding the orbital radius when you know the orbital distance. _____

▬ Solve ▬

4. Complete the table.

   a. Use the formulas to complete the data for Io.

   b. For Ganymede, you know the orbital distance. Find the orbital radius.

   c. Find the orbital radius for Callisto. Then find the speed.

▬ Look Back ▬

5. Would it be easier to complete the table by finding all orbital radii, then all the orbital distances, and so on? Explain. _____

_____

SOLVE ANOTHER PROBLEM

Europa, another of Jupiter's moons has an orbital radius of 0.67 and a period of 3.55 days. Extend the table above and add the data. Then complete the table to find the missing data.

GPS **PROBLEM 35, STUDENT PAGE 129**

In a laboratory experiment, two colonies of bacteria are being observed. One is growing at the rate of 1.5×10^5 bacteria per half-hour. The other is growing at the rate of 3.2×10^5 bacteria per hour. Which is growing faster? How do you know?

— Understand —

1. Are both rates given for the same length of time? _____

— Plan —

2. Why will you need to double the first number in order to compare?

   _____

3. Which number is greater, 1.5×10^5 or 3.2×10^5?
   1.5×10^5
   3.2×10^5 ⟶ The power of 10 is the same.
   Compare 1.5 and 3.2.

   _____

4. Which of these pairs of numbers will you need to compare to decide which product is greater for $2(1.5 \times 10^5)$ and 3.2×10^5. _____

   a. 2(1.5) and 3.2   **b.** 2(3.2) and 1.5   **c.** 1.5 and 3.2

— Solve —

5. Compare the rates. Explain. _____

   _____

— Look Back —

6. How could you find the answer using another method of solving?

   _____

   SOLVE ANOTHER PROBLEM

One colony of bacteria is growing at the rate of 2.59×10^7 times per half hour. The other is growing at the rate of 2.79×10^7 times per hour. Which is growing faster? How do you know?

   _____

   _____

Name _____

GPS PROBLEM 39, STUDENT PAGE 138

Raoul is building a fish tank. He wants it to hold
12 liters (12,000-mL) of water. The formula $V = lwh$
tells the volume (V) in milliliters of a tank with
length (l), width (w), and height (h) in centimeters.
He wants the length, width, and height to be
whole numbers.

   a. List three sets of dimensions that will result in a 12,000-mL tank.

   b. Which shape do you think requires more glass?

━━ **Understand** ━━

1. What product will *lwh* produce? _____

2. How many measures will be in each set of dimensions? _____

━━ **Plan** ━━

3. Write the prime factorization of 12,000. _____

4. How can you use the prime factorization to find three dimensions? _____

   _____

5. How will you find the glass needed to make
   the aquarium? The aquarium will have a glass top. _____

━━ **Solve** ━━

6. Find three sets of whole number dimensions that multiply to 12,000.

   _____

7. Which set of dimensions do you think requires the most glass?

   _____

━━ **Look Back** ━━

8. What other strategy could you use to find the answer?

   _____

┌──────────────────────────────────┐
│   **SOLVE ANOTHER PROBLEM**   │
└──────────────────────────────────┘

Using only whole numbers for dimensions, find three sets
of dimensions that will produce a volume of 23 L (23,000 mL). _____

GPS PROBLEM 20, STUDENT PAGE 142

Bennie is catering a wedding and is putting finger food on plates. He has 72 cheese puffs and 48 carrot sticks. He wants both kinds of food on each plate. He wants to distribute the food evenly, and he doesn't want any left over. What is the largest number of plates he can use, and how many of each type of food should he put on each plate?

▬ Understand ▬

1. Underline what you are asked to find.

2. Circle the quantities of food Bennie has to serve.

▬ Plan ▬

3. Write the prime factorization of 72. _____

4. Write the prime factorization of 48. _____

▬ Solve ▬

5. Use the prime factorizations to find the GCF of 72 and 48. _____

6. What is the largest number of plates Bennie can use? _____

7. The remaining factors in the prime factorization tell how many of each item will be on a plate. How many of each item will be on each plate?

   a. cheese puffs _____   b. carrot sticks _____

▬ Look Back ▬

8. What is another way you could find the largest number of plates? _____

   _____

   _____

SOLVE ANOTHER PROBLEM

Bennie is catering another party and is putting finger food on plates. He has 60 pigs-in-a-blanket and 45 small tacos. He wants both kinds of food on each plate. He wants to distribute the food evenly, and he doesn't want any left over. What is the largest number of plates he can use, and how many of each type of food should he put on each plate?

_____

_____

Name _____

Name _____

Name _____

Name _____

Name _____

Name

Name _____

GPS PROBLEM 40, STUDENT PAGE 148

A batting average in softball or baseball is the number of hits divided by the number of times at bat. A batting average of .285 means that the batter would be expected to get a hit 285 times in 1000 at-bats. The fraction $\frac{285}{1000}$ can be used to represent a batting average of .285. Use equivalent fractions to help you complete the following table. Use a calculator to check your answers.

	Maria	Sophie	Ja	Mia
Hits			24	18
Times at Bat	80	90		
Batting Average	.250	.300	.400	.200

Understand
1. What do you need to do? _____

Plan
2. Write the batting average as a fraction for each player $\left(\dfrac{\text{number of hits}}{\text{number of times at bat}}\cdot\right)$.

Maria _____ Sophie _____ Ja _____ Mia _____

3. Write a fraction for each blank in the table. Let x represent any unknowns. For example, the number of hits for Maria is $\frac{x}{80}$.

Sophie _____ Ja _____ Mia _____

4. Write equivalent fractions for each player using information from Items 2 and 3.

_____

_____

Solve
5. Complete the table.

Look Back
6. Does each girl's batting average equal her hits divided by times at bat? _____

SOLVE ANOTHER PROBLEM

Add this information to the table: Chim: hits, 14; batting average, .350; Que: times at bat, 90; batting average .200. Complete the table.

GPS PROBLEM 19, STUDENT PAGE 151

Theresa is building a guitar for her daughter. The guitar must be between $\frac{1}{2}$ and $\frac{3}{4}$ of the size of a full-sized guitar. Find and list in order, from least to greatest, four fractions in that range. Express the fractions in lowest terms.

▬ Understand ▬

1. What do you need to find? _____

▬ Plan ▬

2. Why do you need to find a common denominator? _____

_____

3. Use Guess and Check to determine which common denominator to choose that will allow you to write four fractions in between. _____

   a. 4   **b.** 8   **c.** 16   **d.** 20

▬ Solve ▬

4. Write $\frac{1}{2}$ and $\frac{3}{4}$ using the chosen denominator. _____

5. Find four fractions between $\frac{1}{2}$ and $\frac{3}{4}$ using the common denominator. List in order from least to greatest.

_____

6. Write the fractions in lowest terms. _____

▬ Look Back ▬

7. Write $\frac{1}{2}$ amd $\frac{3}{4}$ using a larger common denominator. List four fractions in order from least to greatest between the given fractions. Why may your answers in lowest terms be different than the ones in Item 6?

_____

_____

| SOLVE ANOTHER PROBLEM |

Find four fractions between $\frac{1}{2}$ and $\frac{1}{3}$. List them in order from least to greatest in lowest terms.

_____

Name _____

GPS PROBLEM 25, STUDENT PAGE 156

For each problem, is it better to use a fraction or a decimal to solve the problem? Explain.

a. Sam, Dean, and Matt agree to evenly split the cost of dinner, which totals $100.00. How much does each owe?

b. Miriam has a recipe that serves 12 and she wants to serve 4. The recipe calls for 2 cups of sugar. How much sugar should she use?

c. Every third seat in a music hall has a pair of rental binoculars attached to the seat back. There are 1000 seats in the music hall. How many pairs of binoculars are there?

━━ Understand ━━

1. Underline what you are asked to find.

━━ Plan ━━

2. Is money usually written as a fraction or as a decimal? _____

3. Is part of a cup usually written as a fraction or as a decimal in a recipe? _____

4. Would some seats out of many be written as a fraction or a decimal? _____

━━ Solve ━━

5. Would you rather solve using a fraction or a decimal? Explain.

Part a: _____

Part b: _____

Part c: _____

━━ Look Back ━━

6. Calculate the answer to each problem to see if you agree with your choices.

_____

SOLVE ANOTHER PROBLEM

Is it better to use fractions or decimals to solve a problem involving how much you pay for gas at a service station? Explain.

_____

_____

Name _____

GPS PROBLEM 35, STUDENT PAGE 172

About how many $6\frac{3}{4}$-inch pieces can be cut from a board measuring $37\frac{1}{5}$ inches? Estimate to find your answer.

Understand

1. What are you asked to do? _____

_____

2. What is the length of the board? _____

3. What is the length of each piece that will be cut from the board? _____

Plan

4. What operation will you use to find the answer? _____

5. Will you estimate using rounded or compatible numbers? _____

Solve

6. What number will you use for $6\frac{3}{4}$? _____   For $37\frac{1}{5}$? _____

7. Write a number sentence to find the answer _____

8. Write a sentence to tell about how many pieces can be cut. _____

_____

_____

Look Back

9. Explain how you can draw a diagram to check your answer.

_____

_____

_____

SOLVE ANOTHER PROBLEM

About how many $8\frac{1}{8}$-inch pieces can be cut from a board measuring $67\frac{1}{2}$ inches? Estimate to find your answer. _____

Name _____

 PROBLEM 32, STUDENT PAGE 177

Using each number only once, use the numbers 2, 4, 6, and 8 to write
an expression with two proper fractions that have:

a. The largest possible sum   **b.** The largest possible difference
c. The smallest possible sum   **d.** The smallest possible difference

▬ Understand ▬

1. What is a proper fraction? _____

_____

2. How many proper fractions will you write in each expression? _____

3. How many different digits are in each pair of fractions? _____

▬ Plan ▬

4. List all the proper fractions you can
make using the numbers 2, 4, 6, and 8. _____

5. What are the pairs of fractions you
can use when writing the expressions? _____

▬ Solve ▬

6. For each pair of fractions, find
the sum and the difference.

7. Write an expression for each
part of the problem.

Fraction Pairs	Sum	Difference

Part a. _____   Part b. _____

Part c. _____   Part d. _____

▬ Look Back ▬

8. How can you tell that your answers are reasonable without calculating?

_____

_____

SOLVE ANOTHER PROBLEM

Use the numbers 2, 3, 6, and 8 to answer the question above.

a. _____   b. _____   c. _____   d. _____

Name _____

GPS PROBLEM 30, STUDENT PAGE 182

Find three mixed numbers with different denominators that have a sum of $10\frac{3}{4}$.

━━ Understand ━━━

1. How many numbers are you asked to find? _____

2. What kind of numbers are they? _____

3. What do you know about the sum of the numbers? _____

4. Will the denominators be the same or different? _____

━━ Plan ━━━━━━━

5. Solve this simpler related problem.

   a. Find three different whole numbers that have a sum of 11. _____

   b. How could you use the sum of two of the numbers and 11 to find the third? _____

   _____

6. Tell how you could use the same strategy to solve your problem.

   _____

   _____

━━ Solve ━━━━━━

7. What denominators will you choose? _____

8. What are your three mixed numbers? _____

━━ Look Back ━━━

9. What other strategies could you use to solve the problem? _____

   _____

SOLVE ANOTHER PROBLEM

Find three mixed numbers with different denominators that have a sum of $7\frac{4}{5}$. _____

GPS PROBLEM 31, STUDENT PAGE 190

A square yard measures 3 ft by 3 ft. How many square yards of floor space are in a 2 ft by 6 ft closet?

━ Understand ━

1. What are you asked to find? _____

_____

2. Circle the information that you need.

━ Plan ━

At the right is a diagram of 1 square yard. Divide the diagram to show square feet.

4. How many square feet are equal to 1 square yard? _____

5. How many square yards are equal to 18 square feet? _____

6. How many square yards are equal to 27 square feet? _____

7. Analyze your answers to Items 5 and 6. Write an expression to show the number of square yards in *x* square feet. _____

━ Solve ━

8. How many square feet of floor space are in a 2 ft by 6 ft closet? _____

9. How many square yards of floor space are in the closet? _____

━ Look Back ━

10. How can you check your answer? _____

_____

SOLVE ANOTHER PROBLEM

A square foot measures 12 in. by 12 in. How many square feet of shelf paper is needed to line the bottom of a 10 in. by 18 in. drawer? _____

Name _____

GPS **PROBLEM 32, STUDENT PAGE 195**

Find the areas of the rooms diagrammed.
How much larger than the dining room is
the area of the family room?

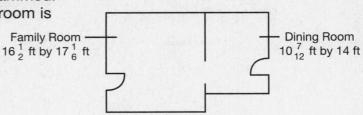

Family Room
$16\frac{1}{2}$ ft by $17\frac{1}{6}$ ft

Dining Room
$10\frac{7}{12}$ ft by 14 ft

━━ Understand ━━

1. What are the dimensions of the family room? _____

2. What are the dimensions of the dining room? _____

━━ Plan ━━

3. How will you find the area of each room? _____

4. Use improper fractions to show
   how to find the area of the family room. _____

5. Use the Distributive Property to show
   how to find the area of the dining room. _____

6. Which operation will you use to find how much
   larger the family room is than the dining room? _____

━━ Solve ━━

7. Find the area of the family room. _____ Of the dining room. _____

8. How much larger is the family room than the dining room? _____

━━ Look Back ━━

9. Would it be easier to find the answer by
   converting the measures to inches? Explain. _____

_____

| **SOLVE ANOTHER PROBLEM** |

Find the areas of the rooms diagrammed.
How much larger than the bathroom is
the area of the bedroom?

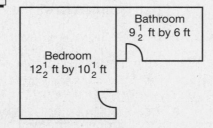

Bathroom
$9\frac{1}{2}$ ft by 6 ft

Bedroom
$12\frac{1}{2}$ ft by $10\frac{1}{2}$ ft

GPS **PROBLEM 32, STUDENT PAGE 200**

A border design measures $4\frac{3}{8}$ inches. How many times does a single row repeat around the top of the walls of a room that measures $12\frac{1}{2}$ ft by $10\frac{1}{4}$ ft?

━━ Understand ━━

1. Circle the information you need.

━━ Plan ━━

2. Draw a diagram of the room, labeling the length and width.

3. Write a numerical expression showing the total distance around the room. _____

4. What operation would you use to find the number of times the design repeats? _____

5. Why do you need to convert the total distance around the room from feet to inches?

_____

━━ Solve ━━

6. What is the total distance in feet? _____ In inches? _____

7. How many times does the design repeat? _____

━━ Look Back ━━

8. Could you solve the problem by converting the length of the border from inches to feet? Explain. _____

_____

_____

SOLVE ANOTHER PROBLEM

A border design measures $3\frac{1}{2}$ inches. How many times does a single row repeat around the top of the walls of a room that measures $10\frac{3}{4}$ ft by $13\frac{3}{4}$ ft? _____

Name _____

GPS | PROBLEM 18, STUDENT PAGE 216

When a beam of light strikes a flat mirror, the light reflects at the same angle at which it hit the mirror's surface.

a. If light strikes a mirror at a 50° angle, at what angle will the light reflect?

b. What is the measure of the angle *between* the angle at which light strikes the mirror (50°), and the angle at which the light reflects?

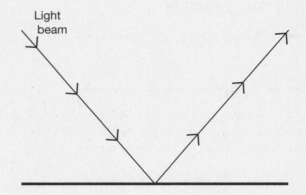

Light beam

Understand

1. In the diagram, label the angle formed when the light

   a. strikes the mirror as ∠1.

   b. reflects from the mirror as ∠2.

2. Label the angle between ∠1 and ∠2 as ∠3.

3. What is the measure of ∠1? _____

Plan

4. Which two angles will be congruent? _____

5. What is the sum of the three angles shown in the diagram? _____

6. Write an expression showing how to find the measure of the noncongruent angle. _____

Solve

7. What is the measure of ∠2? _____ Of ∠3? _____

Look Back

8. How can you check your answer? _____

_____

| SOLVE ANOTHER PROBLEM |

a. If light strikes a mirror at a 65° angle, at what angle will the light reflect? _____

b. What is the measure of the angle *between* the angle at which light strikes the mirror (65°), and the angle at which the light reflects? _____

Name _____

GPS **PROBLEM 15, STUDENT PAGE 220**

Draw a line segment, then measure it and identify its midpoint. Use the midpoint and your protractor to draw a perpendicular bisector.

━━ Understand ━━

1. Underline the two things you are asked to draw.

2. What is a perpendicular bisector? _____

_____

━━ Plan ━━

3. How will you find the midpoint? _____

_____

4. What will be the measure of the angle formed by
the line segment and the perpendicular bisector? _____

━━ Solve ━━

5. Draw your line segment. Measure it and identify its midpoint.
Then use your protractor to draw a perpendicular bisector.

━━ Look Back ━━

6. Does it matter which of the two congruent
segments you use when you measure the angle
needed to draw the perpendicular bisector? Explain. _____

_____

SOLVE ANOTHER PROBLEM

Draw a line segment. Use your protractor
and ruler to draw another line segment
that has one of the endpoints of the first
segment as its midpoint.

Name _____

GPS PROBLEM 16, STUDENT PAGE 226

A molecule of boron fluoride forms a
molecular arrangement, as shown.
An atom of boron is bonded to three
atoms of fluorine. The angle between
each bond measures 120°. Find the
total measure of all the angles formed
between the bonds.

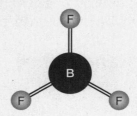

── Understand ──

1. Underline what you are asked to find.

2. How many angles are represented in the diagram? _____

3. What is the measure of the angle formed by each bond? _____

── Plan ──

4. Which letter represents the vertex of the angles formed? _____

5. Write the angle measure for each angle in the diagram. _____

6. Which operation can you use to find the
   total measures of all the angles formed? _____

── Solve ──

7. What is the total measure of all the angles between the bonds? _____

── Look Back ──

8. The outer edges of the model of the fluorine atom are curved.
   Use these edges to connect the three atoms. What figure is
   formed? How can you use this to support your answer to Item 7? _____

_____

_____

| SOLVE ANOTHER PROBLEM |

Curtis drew this diagram. The angle
between each "spoke" measures 90°.
Find the total measure of all the
angles formed between the spokes.

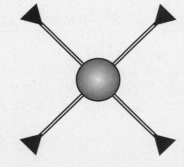

_____

GPS PROBLEM 18, STUDENT PAGE 231

The sum of the measures of the angles of a polygon is 1620°.
How many sides does the polygon have?

━━ Understand ━━

1. What are you asked to find? _____

_____

━━ Plan ━━

2. Choose the expression that shows how to find
   the number of triangles in a figure with n sides. _____

   a. $\frac{n}{2}$ **b.** $n + 2$ **c.** $2n$ **d.** $n - 2$

3. What formula relates the number of sides and
   the sum of the angle measures of a polygon? _____

4. Use the formula to complete the table.

Sides	3	4	5	6
Number of triangles				
Sum of the angles				

5. What do you need to do to find the number of triangles
   in a polygon when you know the sum of the measures
   of the angles? _____

6. What do you need to do to find the number of sides
   when you know the number of triangles in the polygon? _____

━━ Solve ━━

7. Find the number of triangles in a polygon whose sum
   of the angles is 1620°. _____

8. Find the number of sides in a polygon that has the
   same number of triangles as the polygon in Item 7. _____

━━ Look Back ━━

9. What other strategies could you use to solve the problem? _____

_____

SOLVE ANOTHER PROBLEM

The sum of the measures of the angles of a polygon
is 2160°. How many sides does the polygon have? _____

GPS | **PROBLEM 13, STUDENT PAGE 236**

Is it possible for one rectangle to have a greater area than another but a smaller perimeter? If so, give an example. If not, explain why not.

━━ Understand ━━

1. What are you asked to decide? _____

_____

━━ Plan ━━

2. Draw a 1-cm × 6-cm rectangle. Label the sides.

3. Find the perimeter and the area of the rectangle.

_____

4. Choose an area that is greater than, but *not* more than double the area of the rectangle. Then find the factors for that area.

_____

━━ Solve ━━

5. Find the perimeter for each pair of factors. _____

6. Continue trying different areas. Did you find an example of a rectangle with a greater area and smaller perimeter? Explain. _____

_____

_____

━━ Look Back ━━

7. What other strategy could you use to find the answer? _____

SOLVE ANOTHER PROBLEM

Is it possible for one square to have a greater area than another but a smaller perimeter? If so, give an example. If not, explain why not. _____

_____

_____

Name _____

GPS PROBLEM 40, STUDENT PAGE 243

Schoolchildren in Ghana play the game of Achi on a board like the one shown. If the perimeter of an Achi board is 192 cm, what is its area?

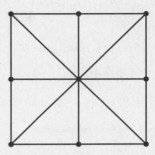

▬ Understand ▬

1. Underline the perimeter.

2. What polygon is the Achi board? _____

▬ Plan ▬

3. What is the formula to find the perimeter of this figure? _____

4. How can you use the formula to find the length of one side? _____

_____

5. How can you find the area once you know the length of one side? _____

_____

▬ Solve ▬

6. What is the length of one side? _____

7. What is the area of the Achi board? _____

▬ Look Back ▬

8. How can you work backward from your answer to find the perimeter? _____

_____

SOLVE ANOTHER PROBLEM

Butch has a square checkerboard. If the perimeter of the checkerboard is 160 cm, what is the area?

_____

Name _____

GPS PROBLEM 20, STUDENT PAGE 247

An 8 ft ladder leans against a building with the base of the ladder 3 ft from the building. How high is the point where the ladder touches the building?

━━ Understand ━━

1. Underline the question.

2. Circle the information you need.

━━ Plan ━━

3. Which of the following strategies could you use to find the height? _____

   a. Make a List   **b.** Draw a Diagram   **c.** Use a Table

4. Use the strategy you chose in Item 3 to show the information in the problem.

5. What figure is formed by the building, the ladder, and the ground? _____

6. What formula will you use to find the height?

   _____

7. Rewrite the formula substituting the values you know. _____

━━ Solve ━━

8. Solve your equation to find the height of the point where the ladder touches the building. Round your answer to the nearest hundredth. _____

━━ Look Back ━━

9. How could you use the strategy, Solve a Simpler Problem to find the height? _____

   _____

SOLVE ANOTHER PROBLEM

A 13 ft ladder leans against a building with the base of the ladder 5 ft from the building. How high is the point where the ladder touches the building? _____

GPS PROBLEM 22, STUDENT PAGE 252

Draw and label the following triangles.
Include labels for both base and height.

a. Two different triangles, each with an area of 6 square units
b. Two different triangles, each with an area of 15 square units
c. Two different triangles, each with an area of 24 square units

▬ Understand ▬

1. Circle the area of the triangles you will draw.

2. What is the formula to find the area of a triangle? _____

▬ Plan ▬

3. What will the product of the base and height have to be for each triangle?

a. _____   **b.** _____   **c.** _____

4. Find two factor pairs for each product in Item 3.

a. _____   **b.** _____   **c.** _____

5. How can you use factor pairs as dimensions of each triangle?

_____

▬ Solve ▬

6. Draw and label *two* triangles for each area.

a. 6 square units   **b.** 15 square units   **c.** 24 square units

▬ Look Back ▬

7. How can you use the two factor pairs you found
in Item 4 to draw and label two more triangles? _____

_____

SOLVE ANOTHER PROBLEM

Draw and label two different triangles,
each with an area of 40 square units.

Name _____

GPS PROBLEM 17, STUDENT PAGE 256

The game of tiddlywinks is thought to have originated in England. Although it is often thought of as a children's game, it is popular on university campuses. How much larger is the area of the 2-point portion of the board than the area of the 10-point portion?

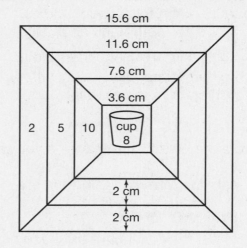

Understand

1. Underline what you are asked to find.

Plan

2. What is the area of the entire gameboard? _____

3. If the gameboard did not have the 2-point strip, what would its area be? _____

4. Which operation would you use to find the area of the 2-point section? _____

5. Which two areas would you use to find the area of the 10-point section?

_____

Solve

6. What is the area of the 2-point section? _____

7. What is the area of the 10-point section? _____

8. How much larger is the area of the 2-point portion of the board than the area of the 10-point portion? _____

Look Back

9. Write an equation using a different operation to find the area of the 2-point portion. _____

_____

SOLVE ANOTHER PROBLEM

How much smaller is the area of the 10-point portion than the area of the 5-point portion? _____

Name _____

GPS PROBLEM 13, STUDENT PAGE 262

A rectangular table measures 48 in. by 30 in. A square chessboard 24 in.
on a side is set on the table. What amount of the table's area is *not*
covered by the chessboard?

▬ Understand ▬

1. What are the dimensions of the table? _____

2. What are the dimensions of the chessboard? _____

▬ Plan ▬

3. Draw a diagram of the chessboard
   on the table. Shade the area you
   are trying to find.

4. Which formula will you use to find the area of the table? _____

5. Which formula will you use to find the area of the chessboard? _____

6. After you know the areas of the table and the chessboard,
   which operation will you use to find the area *not* covered? _____

▬ Solve ▬

7. What is the area of the table? _____

8. What is the area of the chessboard? _____

9. Write a sentence giving the area not covered. _____

_____

▬ Look Back ▬

10. Why is it easier to solve the problem by drawing a diagram? Explain. _____

_____

SOLVE ANOTHER PROBLEM

One wall measures 12 ft by 8 ft and contains a window measuring
3 ft by 4 ft. How much wallpaper will be needed to cover the wall? _____

Name _____

GPS **PROBLEM 15, STUDENT PAGE 277**

The horse pictured stands 16 *hands* tall at the shoulders. Estimate the ratio of the horse's height from the shoulders up to its height from the shoulders down. Use hands as the unit of measurement.

Understand

1. How many heights do you need to estimate? _____

2. Underline what each part of the ratio represents.

Plan

3. How can you divide the horse's entire height into 16 hands?

_____

_____

_____

4. About how many hands is the horse's height from the shoulders up?

_____

5. About how many hands is the horse's height from the shoulders down?

_____

6. Which measure will you use in your ratio for the

   a. numerator? _____   **b.** denominator? _____

Solve

7. Give the estimate of the ratio of the horse's height from the shoulders up to its height from the shoulders down. _____

Look Back

8. Write the ratio in two other ways. _____

| SOLVE ANOTHER PROBLEM |

The vase and its flowers pictured at the right measure 15 inches high. Estimate the ratio of height of the vase to the height of the flowers above the vase. _____

GPS **PROBLEM 26, STUDENT PAGE 281**

Some jobs pay hourly wages; other jobs pay a salary for a week's work. One job pays $7.00 for each hour's work. A second job pays $320.00 for 40 hours of work each week. Which job has a higher unit rate? Explain.

▬ Understand ▬

1. Circle the information you will need to use to solve the problem.

2. A unit rate is a rate where the _____

    a. first quantity is one unit.   **b.** second quantity is one unit.

▬ Plan ▬

3. Which rate has a unit rate of one hour? _____

4. Write the other rate as an hourly rate. _____

5. What operation will you use to change the rate in Item 4 to a unit rate?

_____

▬ Solve ▬

6. Find the unit rate for the rate in Item 4. _____

7. Compare the unit rates. Which job has the higher unit rate? Explain.

_____

_____

▬ Look Back ▬

8. How could you check your answer to see if it is reasonable?

_____

_____

SOLVE ANOTHER PROBLEM

One job pays an annual salary of $24,000 for 12 months' work. Another job pays $1700 per month. Which job has a higher unit rate? Explain.

_____

_____

Name _____

GPS ☐ PROBLEM 18, STUDENT PAGE 285

It is estimated that 13 out of every 100 pounds of garbage in the United States is recycled. An average person in the United States throws away about 4 pounds of garbage per day. About how many pounds of garbage does an average person recycle in 50 days? 100 days?

━━ Understand ━━

1. Circle the information you will need to use to solve the problem.

━━ Plan ━━

2. About how many pounds of garbage does an average person throw away in 50 days? _____

3. About how many pounds of garbage does an average person throw away in 100 days? _____

━━ Solve ━━

4. Choose an equivalent ratio that gives the approximate number of pounds of garbage recycled by an average person in 50 days. _____

   a. $\frac{13}{100} = \frac{26}{200}$ b. $\frac{13}{100} = \frac{52}{100}$

5. Write an equivalent ratio that gives the approximate number of pounds of garbage recycled by an average person in 100 days. _____

6. About how many pounds of garbage does an average person recycle in 50 days? In 100 days? _____

━━ Look Back ━━

7. Does it make sense that the number of pounds of garbage recycled in 100 days is double that recycled in 50 days? Explain.

_____

_____

_____

☐ SOLVE ANOTHER PROBLEM ☐

Out of every 4 books read by Janelle, 3 are fiction. She reads 14 books each semester. How many fiction books does she read in 6 semesters? _____

GPS **PROBLEM 16, STUDENT PAGE 290**

Estelle has built two towers of blocks. There are 12 blocks in Tower A and 18 blocks in Tower B. If she takes one block from each tower, will the ratio of blocks remain the same? Is there any number she could remove from each tower to keep the ratio the same? Explain.

━━ Understand ━━

1. Circle the number of blocks in Tower A.

2. Underline the number of blocks in Tower B.

━━ Plan ━━

3. Write the current ratio of number of blocks in Tower A to the number of blocks in Tower B in lowest terms. _____

4. Complete the table to show the number of blocks in each tower if Estelle removes more than one block from the tower.

Tower A	12	11									
Tower B	18	17									

━━ Solve ━━

5. Is the ratio the same if she removes one block from each tower? _____

6. Is there any number of blocks she can remove from each tower to keep the same ratio? Explain.

_____

_____

━━ Look Back ━━

7. How can a table of ratios equivalent to $\frac{2}{3}$ help you check your answer?

_____

_____

_____

SOLVE ANOTHER PROBLEM

Tower X has 15 blocks and Tower Y has 20 blocks. Is there any number of blocks that can be removed from each tower to keep the ratio of blocks the same? _____

Name _____

GPS PROBLEM 23, STUDENT PAGE 297

Find values of the variables so that the three ratios are equivalent.
$\frac{2}{9}$, $\frac{x}{45}$, and $\frac{14}{y}$

━━ Understand ━━

1. What are you asked to find?

_____

━━ Plan ━━

2. All three ratios must be equivalent to what given ratio? _____

━━ Solve ━━

3. Complete the table to find ratios equivalent to $\frac{2}{9}$. Let x represent
the top number of the ratios and y represent the bottom number
of the ratios in the table.

x	2									
y	9									

4. What is the value of x when the bottom number is 45? _____

5. What is the value of y when the top number is 14? _____

6. Write the three equivalent ratios. _____

━━ Look Back ━━

6. How can you tell if all three ratios are equivalent?

_____

_____

_____

| SOLVE ANOTHER PROBLEM |

Find values of the variables so these three ratios are equivalent.
$\frac{5}{9}$, $\frac{20}{c}$, and $\frac{d}{63}$.

_____

Name _____

GPS **PROBLEM 19, STUDENT PAGE 301**

Researchers tracking a pod (group) of killer whales found that the whales swam 30 miles in 4 hours on Monday, 45 miles in 6 hours on Tuesday, and 60 miles in 8 hours on Wednesday. Make a scatterplot to find out if these rates are proportional.

Understand

1. Underline what you are asked to do.

2. Circle the information you will use.

Plan

3. Make a table to show the values you will plot.

Miles			
Hours			

4. Make a scatterplot of the values in your table. Connect the points.

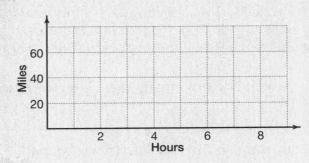

Solve

5. Are these rates proportional? Explain. _____

_____

Look Back

6. How can you determine if the rates are proportional without making a scatterplot?

_____

SOLVE ANOTHER PROBLEM

A gazelle travels 25 miles in 2 hours on Monday, 36 mi in 5 hours on Tuesday, and 37 mi in 1 hour on Wednesday. Make a scatterplot to find out if these rates are proportional.

_____

_____

Name _____

GPS **PROBLEM 9, STUDENT PAGE 306**

Phileas Fogg was the hero of Jules Verne's adventure novel *Around the World in Eighty Days*. The distance around the earth is about 25,000 miles.

a. Assuming Fogg traveled at a steady rate, how long did it take him to travel the 4000 miles from London to India?

b. How far did Fogg travel during the final week of his trip?

━━ Understand ━━

1. Underline the two things you are asked to find.

2. What is the distance around the earth? _____

━━ Plan ━━

3. What is the unit rate in miles per day traveled by Phileas Fogg? _____

   a. $\frac{50 \text{ mi}}{1 \text{ day}}$ **b.** $\frac{312.5 \text{ mi}}{1 \text{ day}}$ **c.** $\frac{6.25 \text{ mi}}{1 \text{ day}}$

4. Which proportion would you use to find how many days it took Fogg to travel 4000 miles? _____

   a. $\frac{50 \text{ mi}}{1 \text{ day}} = \frac{? \text{ days}}{4000 \text{ mi}}$ **b.** $\frac{312.5 \text{ mi}}{1 \text{ day}} = \frac{4000 \text{ mi}}{? \text{ days}}$

5. How can you find how many days it took Phileas Fogg to travel 4000 miles?

   _____

6. How can you use the unit rate to find how far Fogg traveled during the final week?

   _____

━━ Solve ━━

7. How long did it take Fogg to get from London to India? _____

8. How far did Fogg travel during the final week? _____

━━ Look Back ━━

9. How can you determine if your answers are reasonable?

   _____

   _____

SOLVE ANOTHER PROBLEM

Suppose a traveler covers 9800 miles in 35 days.
At this rate, how far can she travel in 50 days? _____

GPS PROBLEM 28, STUDENT PAGE 312

The ratio of teachers to students at Sam Houston Middle School
is 1 to 36. If there are 720 students, how many more teachers are
needed to make the teacher-to-student ratio 1 to 30? Explain.

═ Understand ═

1. What is the current ratio of teachers to students? _____

2. What is the proposed ratio of teachers to students? _____

═ Plan ═

3. Which proportion would you use to find the number
   of teachers currently at Sam Houston Middle School. _____

   a. $\dfrac{1}{30} = \dfrac{x}{720}$ **b.** $\dfrac{1}{36} = \dfrac{720}{x}$ **c.** $\dfrac{1}{36} = \dfrac{x}{720}$

4. Which proportion would you use to find the number of
   teachers needed to make the teacher-to-student ratio 1 to 30. _____

   a. $\dfrac{1}{36} = \dfrac{x}{720}$ **b.** $\dfrac{1}{30} = \dfrac{x}{720}$ **c.** $\dfrac{1}{30} = \dfrac{720}{x}$

═ Solve ═

5. How many teachers are currently
   teaching at Sam Houston Middle School? _____

6. How many teachers are needed if
   the teacher-to-student ratio is 1 to 30? _____

7. How many more teachers are needed to
   make the teacher-to-student ratio 1 to 30? _____

═ Look Back ═

7. How can you check your answers? _____

_____

_____

_____

_____

SOLVE ANOTHER PROBLEM

The ratio of computers to printers in Juan's computer
classroom is 5 to 1. There are 60 computers. How
many more printers are needed to make the ratio 4 to 1? _____

GPS PROBLEM 21, STUDENT PAGE 327

A group of artists produced a miniature model of New York City in which every detail of the city is modeled at a much smaller scale. A 1200 ft tall building measures just 1 ft tall in the model. Express the scale used in the model in in. per ft.

▬▬ Understand ▬▬

1. How tall is the model? _____

2. How tall is the actual building? _____

3. What will your ratio of the scale compare? _____

_____

4. What units of measure are used in the scale? _____

▬▬ Plan ▬▬

5. Which ratio best represents the scale of the model? _____

  a. $\dfrac{12\ ft}{1200\ ft}$ **b.** $\dfrac{12\ in.}{1200\ ft}$ **c.** $\dfrac{12\ in.}{12\ ft}$

6. How can you rewrite the ratio so that the first number in the ratio is 1 inch?

_____

▬▬ Solve ▬▬

7. Write a sentence to express the scale in inches per foot.

_____

_____

▬▬ Look Back ▬▬

8. Use the ratio you expressed in Item 7. Find the number of inches that would represent 1200 ft. Is it equivalent to 1 ft? _____

| SOLVE ANOTHER PROBLEM |

A 100-yard football field is displayed in a model that is 6 inches long. Express the scale used in the model in inches per foot. _____

GPS **PROBLEM 17, STUDENT PAGE 332**

Stan Herd is an artist who plants flowers and grains on large fields to create "crop art." He often makes a scale drawing before planting seeds and flowers. If a sketch measures 6.4 in. × 10.2 in. at a scale of 1 in. = 25 ft, what will be the dimensions of his "crop art"?

━━ Understand ━━

1. What are the measurements of Herd's drawing? _____

2. What is the scale used in the drawing? _____

3. What are you asked to find? _____

━━ Plan ━━

4. What would be a reasonable dimension of the "crop art"? _____

    a. 600 in. × 100 ft   **b.** 160 ft × 170 ft   **c.** 150 ft × 250 ft

━━ Solve ━━

5. What is the width of the "crop art"? _____

6. What is the length of the "crop art"? _____

7. Write a sentence giving the actual dimensions of the "crop art."

_____

_____

━━ Look Back ━━

8. What proportion could you use to find each dimension?

_____

SOLVE ANOTHER PROBLEM

An aerial photographer took a picture of a city block. The picture measured 8.5 in. × 11 in. The scale of the picture was 1 in. = 30 ft. What are the actual dimensions of the city block?

_____

Name _____

GPS PROBLEM 12, STUDENT PAGE 336

Students at Northampton East High School in North Carolina designed
an electric car. At top speed, the car can travel for 6 hr. Then its
batteries must be recharged for 6 hr. If this car travels 1440 miles,
when would the car arrive if it left on Tuesday at noon? (Assume the
driver travels at a speed of 65 mi/hr.)

▬ Understand ▬

1. Underline what you are asked to find.

▬ Plan ▬

2. Complete the table that shows how many miles were traveled at
   the end of each 6-hour period.

Hours	6	12	18				
Miles	390	390	780				

3. The electric car travels 1440 miles in all. How
   many more miles would it have traveled in 42 hours? _____

4. About how many hours does it
   take to travel the distance in Item 3? _____

5. About how many hours did the trip take? _____

▬ Solve ▬

6. At what time did the car arrive? _____

▬ Look Back ▬

7. How can you solve this problem using different steps in order to
   see if your answer is reasonable?

   _____

   _____

   _____

SOLVE ANOTHER PROBLEM

Suppose the driver of the car left at 10 A.M.
on Monday and traveled 1050 miles. About
what time would they arrive at the destination? _____

GPS PROBLEM 11, STUDENT PAGE 340

The Oscar Mayer Wienermobile has been a traveling
advertisement for the past 60 years. The 27 ft long
Wienermobile looks like a large hot dog sitting on a bun.
A hot dog measures about 5 in. in length. What is the
scale of the Wienermobile compared to a real hot dog?

▬ Understand ▬

1. What is the length of the Wienermobile? _____

2. What is the length of a real hot dog? _____

3. What are you asked to find? _____

_____

_____

▬ Plan ▬

4. Which ratio represents the Wienermobile compared to a real hot dog? _____

   a. $\dfrac{5 \text{ in.}}{60 \text{ ft}}$ b. $\dfrac{27 \text{ ft}}{60 \text{ yr}}$ c. $\dfrac{27 \text{ ft}}{5 \text{ in.}}$ d. $\dfrac{60 \text{ yr}}{5 \text{ in.}}$

5. What will you divide by so that the scale length of the hot dog is 1 in.?

_____

▬ Solve ▬

6. What is the scale of the Wienermobile compared to the length of
   a real hot dog?

_____

▬ Look Back ▬

7. What is the scale of the real hot dog compared to the Wienermobile?

_____

SOLVE ANOTHER PROBLEM

The Space Shuttle is 56 m tall. A model of the
Space Shuttle is 84 cm tall. What is the scale
of the model compared to the Space Shuttle? _____

Name _____

GPS PROBLEM 23, STUDENT PAGE 348

Two buses leave your school to take students on field trips. One bus travels for 20 minutes, covering 15 miles. The other travels 45 miles in one hour. Did both buses travel at the same rate? Explain your answer.

── Understand ──

1. Underline the time and distance traveled by each bus.

2. How can you tell if the rates are the same? _____

_____

── Plan ──

3. Which rate is usually used to describe vehicle travel? _____

   a. $\frac{hours}{miles}$ b. $\frac{minutes}{miles}$ c. $\frac{miles}{hours}$

4. Use $\frac{1}{3}$ hr to represent 20 min. Which rate represents the first bus? _____

   a. 15 mi:$\frac{1}{3}$ hr   b. 20 min:$\frac{1}{3}$ hr

5. Write the rate in Item 4 as a unit rate. _____

6. Write the unit rate for the second bus. _____

── Solve ──

7. Write both unit rates to see if they are equal. _____

8. Did both buses travel at the same rate? Explain. _____

_____

── Look Back ──

9. Write the rate using miles:minutes. Are they equal?

_____

SOLVE ANOTHER PROBLEM

Jared's dog eats 12 cans of food in 4 days. Keisha's dog eats 56 cans of food in 2 weeks. Are the dogs eating their food at the same rate? Explain.

_____

GPS **PROBLEM 19, STUDENT PAGE 351**

Twenty Thousand Leagues Under the Sea is a famous novel by Jules Verne. A league is about 3.45 miles. Convert 20,000 leagues to feet.

■ Understand ■

1. How many miles is equal to a league? _____

2. What are you asked to do? _____

■ Plan ■

3. How many miles are there in 20,000 leagues? _____

4. How many feet are there in a mile? _____

5. What will you need to do to find how many feet in a league?

_____

■ Solve ■

6. How many feet are in 20,000 leagues? _____

7. Write the title of Verne's novel using feet in place of leagues.

_____

_____

_____

■ Look Back ■

8. Estimate to see if your answer is reasonable.

_____

_____

_____

SOLVE ANOTHER PROBLEM

Convert 15,000 leagues to feet. _____

Name _____

GPS **PROBLEM 16, STUDENT PAGE 356**

Do you use more water for a shower or for a bath? Suppose you always use 250 L of water for a bath and your shower uses 15 L of water per minute.

a. How many minutes would a 150 L shower take?

b. What is the greatest whole number of minutes you can shower and still use less water than you would use taking a bath?

▬ Understand ▬

1. How much water is used for a bath? _____

2. What determines the amount of water used for a shower?

_____

▬ Plan ▬

3. Which expression shows time spent showering if x represents liters of water. _____

   a. $15x$ **b.** $\frac{x}{15}$ **c.** $\frac{150}{x}$ **d.** $150x$

4. Use your expression to complete the table showing number of liters of water used for showers lasting 10 minutes to 20 minutes.

Minutes		11									
Liters of water	150										

▬ Solve ▬

5. How many minutes would a 150-L shower take? _____

6. What is the greatest number of minutes you can shower and still use less water than you would use taking a bath? _____

▬ Look Back ▬

7. In the table above, which amount of water used for showering was closest to 250 L? Explain why this was *not* the correct solution.

_____

SOLVE ANOTHER PROBLEM

Rosetta installed a low-flow shower head that uses 12 L of water per minute. How long can she shower and still use less water than taking a 250-L bath? _____

Suppose $\triangle ABC \sim \triangle DEF$. The length of $\overline{AB}$ is 8, the length of $\overline{BC}$ is 10, the length of $\overline{CA}$ is 12, and the length of $\overline{DE}$ is 12. Find the lengths of $\overline{EF}$ and $\overline{FD}$.

━━ Understand ━━

1. Underline what you need to find.

2. What are the given lengths of these sides?

   AB _____   BC _____   CA _____   DE _____

━━ Plan ━━

3. Draw and label two similar triangles.

4. $\overline{AB}$ and $\overline{DE}$ are corresponding sides of the triangles. List the other corresponding sides.

   _____

5. Which proportion will you use to find EF? _____

   a. $\dfrac{8}{12} = \dfrac{10}{x}$ **b.** $\dfrac{8}{10} = \dfrac{x}{12}$ **c.** $\dfrac{10}{12} = \dfrac{8}{x}$

6. Write a proportion you can use to find FD. _____

━━ Solve ━━

7. What is the length of $\overline{EF}$? _____

8. What is the length of $\overline{FD}$? _____

━━ Look Back ━━

9. How can you check to see if your answers are correct?

   _____

   _____

SOLVE ANOTHER PROBLEM

Suppose $\triangle KLM \sim \triangle XYZ$. The length of $\overline{KL}$ is 6. The length of $\overline{LM}$ is 7, and the length of $\overline{MK}$ is 8. The length of $\overline{XY}$ is 12. Find the lengths of $\overline{YZ}$ and $\overline{ZX}$.

_____

GPS PROBLEM 12, STUDENT PAGE 370

You need to find the distance across the Ralimis River. If $\triangle ABC \sim \triangle DEC$, what is the distance across the river from E to D? Explain how you solved this problem.

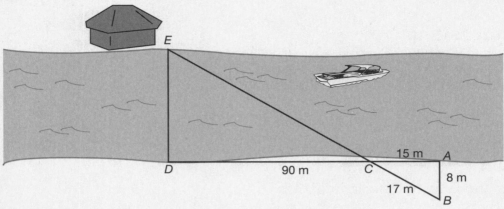

Understand

1. Underline what you need to find.

Plan

2. Write the three pairs of corresponding sides.

   _____   _____   _____

3. What proportion can you use to find DE? _____

   a. $\dfrac{90}{15} = \dfrac{x}{8}$ **b.** $\dfrac{90}{x} = \dfrac{17}{8}$ **c.** $\dfrac{90}{x} = \dfrac{8}{15}$

Solve

4. Find the value of x in your proportion. _____

5. Write a sentence to explain how you solved the problem _____

   _____

   _____

Look Back

6. How can you check your answer? _____

   _____

   SOLVE ANOTHER PROBLEM

What is the distance across the river from
E to C? Round your answer to the nearest tenth. _____

Name _____

GPS **PROBLEM 16, STUDENT PAGE 374**

You find that it takes 0.16 gallons of paint to paint a rectangular wall whose length is 6 ft and whose height is 8 ft. How much paint will you need to paint a wall whose length is 12 ft and whose height is 16 ft?

━━ Understand ━━

1. What are the dimensions of the wall you painted? _____

2. What are the dimensions of the wall you are planning to paint? _____

3. Underline what you are asked to find.

━━ Plan ━━

4. What is the ratio of the

   a. length of the smaller wall to the length of the larger wall? _____

   b. height of the smaller wall to the height of the larger wall? _____

5. Are the ratios you found in Items 3 and 4 equal? _____

6. How is the ratio of the areas of two similar figures related to the scale factor?

   _____

━━ Solve ━━

7. How many times greater is the area of the wall you are planning to paint than the area of the wall you have painted? _____

8. How much paint will you use for the larger wall? _____

━━ Look Back ━━

9. What other strategy can you use to help you solve the problem? _____

   _____

SOLVE ANOTHER PROBLEM

You have wallpapered a section of wall that measures 4 ft high and 7 ft wide. You now need to wallpaper a wall that measures 20 ft high and 35 ft wide. The amount of wallpaper that you will need for the larger wall is how many times the amount of wallpaper that you have already used? _____

GPS **PROBLEM 34, STUDENT PAGE 389**

Although some bats living in the United States migrate during the cold months of the year, other bats spend the winter hibernating in caves. Most bats in the United States hibernate from early October until the end of April. What percent of the year is this?

━━ Understand ━━

1. What are you asked to find? _____

_____

2. What months do most bats hibernate? _____

━━ Plan ━━

3. How many months do most bats hibernate? _____

4. How many months are in a year? _____

5. Write a fraction to show the part of a year most bats hibernate. _____

━━ Solve ━━

6. Divide 100 by the denominator of your fraction in Item 5 to prepare to write an equivalent fraction. _____

7. Complete the equation to write an equivalent fraction to the one you wrote in Item 5.

$$\underline{\hspace{1cm}} \times \underline{\hspace{1cm}} = \frac{\overline{\underline{\hspace{0.5cm}}}}{100}$$

8. Write the percent of the year that most bats hibernate. _____

━━ Look Back ━━

9. Why do you need to know that the dates are *early* October and the *end* of April and not just October and April?

_____

_____

_____

SOLVE ANOTHER PROBLEM

Some students attend school from early September until the end of May. What percent of the year is this? _____

GPS **PROBLEM 40, STUDENT PAGE 393**

Many bats hibernate during the winter. A wide-awake bat may breathe
200 times per minute; a hibernating bat may breathe 23 times per
minute. The bat's normal heart rate of 400 beats per minute often
slows to about 25 beats per minute during hibernation. Express the
breathing rate and heart rate of a hibernating bat as fractions,
decimals, and percents of the corresponding rates for active bats.

━━ Understand ━━━

1. What is the breathing rate of a hibernating bat? _____

2. What is the breathing rate of an active bat? _____

3. What is the heart rate of a hibernating bat? _____

4. What is the heart rate of an active bat? _____

5. Which ratio are you asked to find for each rate? _____

a. $\dfrac{\text{hibernating rate}}{\text{active (wide-awake) rate}}$ **b.** $\dfrac{\text{active (wide-awake) rate}}{\text{hibernating rate}}$

━━ Plan ━━━

6. Write the ratio for the breathing rate. _____ For the heart rate. _____

━━ Solve ━━━

7. Write the ratio for the breathing rate as a

     a. fraction. _____   **b.** decimal. _____   **c.** percent. _____

8. Write the ratio for the heart rate as a

     a. fraction. _____   **b.** decimal. _____   **c.** percent. _____

━━ Look Back ━━━

9. Write each of your answers in fraction form. Are they all equal?

_____

SOLVE ANOTHER PROBLEM

There are 50 travel books in the library. Of these, 17 are
about international travel. Express the ratio of international
books to travel books as a fraction, a decimal, and a percent. _____

GPS **PROBLEM 46, STUDENT PAGE 398**

A small percent of bats carries rabies—generally, about $\frac{1}{2}$%. In how
large a group of bats would you expect to find exactly one bat carrying
rabies? Explain how you found your answer.

━━ Understand ━━

1. Underline what you are asked to find.

2. What percent of bats carries rabies? _____

━━ Plan ━━

3. Write $\frac{1}{2}$% as a fraction. _____

4. Write your fraction from Item 3 with a whole number in the numerator. _____

5. Explain what your fraction means by giving the
   number of bats that may have rabies and the group size. _____

   _____

━━ Solve ━━

6. Write an equivalent fraction to the fraction
   you wrote in Item 4 with a numerator of 1. _____

7. About how large would you expect a
   group of bats to be if one bat carries rabies? _____

8. Explain how you found your answer. _____

   _____

   _____

━━ Look Back ━━

9. Does your answer mean that every group of bats
   this size will have exactly one bat with rabies? Explain. _____

   _____

   _____

SOLVE ANOTHER PROBLEM

Of all people surveyed, $\frac{1}{4}$% did not favor a proposed land
development project. How large would the survey group have
to be so that this percent would represent exactly one person? _____

GPS **PROBLEM 32, STUDENT PAGE 402**

People in the United States eat about 1.6 billion (1,600,000,000) gallons of ice cream each year. About 30% of this ice cream is vanilla, about 10% is chocolate, and about 5% is chocolate chip.

   a. Use mental math to find the number of gallons sold for each flavor.

   b. There are about 260 million people in the United States. On the average, how many gallons of vanilla ice cream does each one eat in a year?

━━ Understand ━━

1. Circle the information you need.

━━ Plan ━━

2. Which of the ice cream sales is the easiest one to find? Why? _____

_____

3. How can you use your answer to Item 2 to find the other quantities? _____

_____

4. Will you multiply or divide to find the average amount eaten? _____

━━ Solve ━━

5. About how many gallons of vanilla is sold? _____

   Chocolate? _____   Chocolate chip? _____

6. On the average, about how many gallons of vanilla ice cream does each person in the United States eat each year? _____

━━ Look Back ━━

7. Add the sales of chocolate and chocolate chip ice cream. Why should the sum equal one half of the sales of vanilla ice cream? _____

_____

┌─────────────────────────────────┐
│   **SOLVE ANOTHER PROBLEM**   │
└─────────────────────────────────┘

About 55% of the 1.6 billion gallons of ice cream sold is flavors other than vanilla, chocolate, and chocolate chip.

   a. Find the number of gallons sold for these flavors. _____

   b. On the average, how many gallons of these flavors does each of 260 million people eat in a year? _____

Name _____

GPS PROBLEM 15, STUDENT PAGE 408

Superplex Cinemas gives students a 25% discount off the regular ticket price of $7.00.

   a. What percent of the regular price is the student price?

   b. What is the student ticket price?

── Understand ──

1. What is the regular price? _____

2. What percent is the student discount? _____

── Plan ──

3. What percent of the regular price is $7.00? _____

4. Complete the equation to find what percent of the regular price is the student price?

    _____ % − _____ % = _____ %

5. Write an equation to find the student price. _____

6. What is a reasonable student ticket price? _____

   a. $12.75   **b.** $7.00   **c.** $5.25   **d.** $2.75

── Solve ──

7. Solve the equation from Item 5. _____

8. Write the student ticket price and what percent it is of the regular price. _____

── Look Back ──

9. How can you find the student ticket price without first finding what percent it is of the regular price? _____

_____

_____

SOLVE ANOTHER PROBLEM

A sweater is selling at a 35% discount off the regular price of $55.

   a. What percent of the regular price is the sale price? _____

   b. What is the sale price of the sweater? _____

GPS **PROBLEM 15, STUDENT PAGE 413**

The bee hummingbird is the smallest bird. It can weigh as little
as 2 grams. The largest bird, the ostrich, can weigh as much as
150 kilograms. What percent of the weight of a bee hummingbird
is the weight of an ostrich?

▬ Understand ▬

1. What is the weight of a bee hummingbird? _____

2. What is the weight of an ostrich? _____

3. Are the weights given in the same units? _____

4. Which bird weighs more? _____

▬ Plan ▬

5. Is an ostrich's weight more or less than
   100% of a hummingbird's weight? Explain. _____

   _____

   _____

6. How many grams are in a kilogram? _____

7. What is the weight of an ostrich in grams? _____

8. Write a ratio of an ostrich's
   weight to a hummingbird's weight. _____

▬ Solve ▬

9. Write a proportion to find the missing percent. _____

10. Solve the proportion to find the percent. _____

▬ Look Back ▬

11. Write and solve an equation to find the
    percent. Verify that your answer is the same. _____

    _____

SOLVE ANOTHER PROBLEM

An average adult's stride is 2.5 feet. A mile is 1760 yards.
What percent of an average adult's stride is one mile? _____

Name _____

 PROBLEM 26, STUDENT PAGE 419

A softball diamond is a 60 ft by 60 ft square. The sides of a baseball diamond are 50% longer than this. What is the percent increase in the area from the softball diamond to the baseball diamond?

━━ Understand ━━

1. Will you find the percent increase or decrease? _____

2. What are the dimensions of a softball diamond? _____

3. How much longer is the side of a baseball diamond than the side of a softball diamond? _____

━━ Plan ━━

4. Draw a diagram to show the areas of the two fields.

5. Which expression gives you the length of one side of the baseball diamond? _____

   a. 60 + 0.5(60)   **b.** 60 − (60 · 0.5)   **c.** (60 · 0.5) ÷ 60

6. What is the length of the side of the baseball diamond? _____

7. What is the formula for area of a square? _____

━━ Solve ━━

8. What is the area of the softball diamond? _____

9. What is the area of the baseball diamond? _____

10. How much larger is area of the baseball diamond? _____

11. What is the percent increase? _____

━━ Look Back ━━

12. What other strategies could you use to find the answer? _____

_____

| SOLVE ANOTHER PROBLEM |

A gold picture frame is a 20 in. by 20 in. square. The sides of a silver frame are 20% shorter. What is the percent decrease in the area from the gold frame to the silver frame? _____

Name _____

GPS PROBLEM 32, STUDENT PAGE 436

The earth is covered with a rocky *crust*, which can be 25 miles thick. Underneath this is an 1800-mile-thick *mantle* of heavier rock. Below the mantle is a liquid *outer core*, about 1400 miles thick. The center of the earth is a solid *inner core*.

Use integers to describe the minimum and maximum depths of each region. (You will be able to give only the minimum depth of the inner core.)

━━ Understand ━━

1. How many layers will you need to describe? _____

2. Underline which layer will not have a maximum depth.

━━ Plan ━━

3. How can you find the minimum depth for each layer? The maximum depth?

_____

_____

━━ Solve ━━

4. Use integers to describe the minimum and maximum depth of each region.

   a. Crust _____

   b. Mantle _____

   c. Outer core _____

   d. Inner core _____

━━ Look Back ━━

5. What strategy might help you solve this problem? _____

┌─────────────────────────────────────┐
│   SOLVE ANOTHER PROBLEM   │
└─────────────────────────────────────┘

Jo made a deep dive in four stages. She dived 52 feet, then 37 feet lower, then 43 feet lower, and finally 24 feet lower. Use an integer to express her position after each dive.

_____

GPS PROBLEM 24, STUDENT PAGE 440

The chart shows the depth below sea level of several boreholes.

Location	Depth
Belridge, California	11,357 ft
Kola Peninsula, Russia	31,911 ft
St. Bernard Parish, Louisiana	25,600 ft
Szechwan Province, China	2,000 ft

a. Represent each depth as an integer.

b. Order the integers in part **a** from least to greatest.

━━ Understand ━━

1. Underline what you are asked to do.

━━ Plan ━━

2. Which depths can be represented by a negative integer?

_____

3. How can you tell which of two negative integers is less?

_____

━━ Solve ━━

4. Write the integers to represent each depth. _____

_____

5. Mark each integer on the number line.

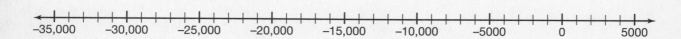

-35,000   -30,000   -25,000   -20,000   -15,000   -10,000   -5000   0   5000

6. Write the integers in order from least to greatest.

_____

━━ Look Back ━━

7. How could you order the negative integers without using a number line?

_____

SOLVE ANOTHER PROBLEM

The chart shows the depth below sea level of several locations. Order the integers from least to greatest.

Location	Depth
Dead Sea	1312 ft
Valdes Peninsula	131 ft
Death Valley	282 ft
Lake Assal	512 ft

Name _____

GPS PROBLEM 19, STUDENT PAGE 445

The depth of a geologic formation is not always the same. Two hundred feet from point *A*, the formation shown is 100 feet deep. It is 200 feet deep at a distance of 500 feet from *A*.

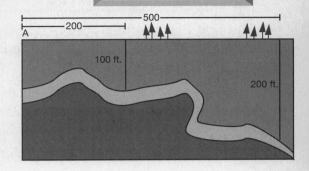

a. Use two ordered pairs to describe this data. Let the *x*-coordinate of each point be the distance from *A* and the *y*-coordinate be the depth of the formation.

b. Plot these ordered pairs on a coordinate plane. Choose a scale that fits the data.

━━ Understand ━━

1. How many points are you asked to describe? _____

2. Circle the information that tells what each coordinate will represent.

━━ Plan ━━

3. Will a positive or negative number represent the

a. *x*-coordinate? _____   **b.** *y*-coordinate? _____

━━ Solve ━━

4. Choose the two ordered pairs that represent the data. _____

   a. (200, 500) and (−100, −200)

   b. (200, −100) and (500, −200)

5. Which scale best fits the data? _____

   a. 100 ft per unit   **b.** 50 ft per unit

6. Plot the points on the grid at the right. Label the *x*-axis, the *y*-axis, and the scale of the graph.

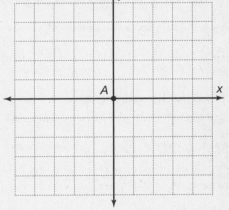

━━ Look Back ━━

7. Could you use a different scale to graph the data? Explain. _____

_____

SOLVE ANOTHER PROBLEM

Kareem's boat is anchored 300 ft east of shore. He dived 50 ft down into the lake. Write an ordered pair that describes his position in relation to the shore and the surface of the lake. Plot the point on the grid above and label it point *X*. _____

GPS **PROBLEM 35, STUDENT PAGE 454**

The first Ferris wheel operated at Chicago's World's Columbian Exposition in 1893. The top of the Ferris wheel was 264 feet above the ground.

a. Bertram's car was at the top of the Ferris wheel. Then it descended 127 feet. Write a sum you could use to find the height of Bertram's car after this descent.

b. How far off the ground was Bertram?

▬ Understand ▬

1. How far is the top of the Ferris wheel from the ground? _____

2. How far did Bertram's car descend from the top of the Ferris wheel? _____

3. What are you asked to do and to find? _____

_____

▬ Plan ▬

4. Write each distance as a positive or negative number.

   a. Top of Ferris wheel from the ground _____

   b. How far the Ferris wheel descended _____

▬ Solve ▬

5. Write a sum to find the height of Bertram's car after its descent. _____

6. How far off the ground was Bertram after the Ferris wheel descended from the top? _____

▬ Look Back ▬

7. Describe another way to find a solution to part b.

_____

SOLVE ANOTHER PROBLEM

The Sears Tower located in Chicago is 110 stories tall. Keisha was on the top floor and used the elevator to descend 98 stories. Write a sum to find the floor Keisha was on after she got off the elevator. What floor was she on?

_____

Name _____

GPS **PROBLEM 29, STUDENT PAGE 458**

The table shows the highest and lowest temperatures ever recorded in
several states. Find the temperature range for each state. Which state
has the widest range? The narrowest range?

Extreme Temperatures					
State	Alaska	California	Hawaii	North Dakota	West Virginia
High Temperature	100°F	134°F	100°F	121°F	112°F
Low Temperature	–80°F	–45°F	14°F	–60°F	–37°F

▬ Understand ▬

1. What is meant by the widest range? The narrowest range?

_____

_____

▬ Plan ▬

2. How can you find each temperature range? _____

   a. Add high and low temperatures.   **b.** Subtract low from high temperature.

▬ Solve ▬

3. Find the temperature range for each state.

   a. Alaska _____   **b.** California _____   **c.** Hawaii _____

   d. North Dakota _____   **e.** West Virginia _____

4. Which state has the widest range? The narrowest? _____

▬ Look Back ▬

5. Use a calculator to check your calculations.

SOLVE ANOTHER PROBLEM

The table shows the highest
and lowest temperatures ever
recorded in Illinois, Nevada,
and Florida. Which state has the
widest range?

Extreme Temperatures (in °F)			
State	Illinois	Florida	Nevada
High Temperature	117°F	109°F	122°F
Low Temperature	–35°F	–2°F	–50°F

_____

GPS PROBLEM 34, STUDENT PAGE 465

Suppose an amusement park bought a merry-go-round for $92,000, and 42,512 people paid $2 each to ride the merry-go-round in its first year of operation. Ignoring the cost of operation, how much money did the park earn or lose on this ride in its first year?

⸺ Understand ⸺

1. Underline what you are asked to find.

2. How much money did the park pay for the merry-go-round? _____

3. How many rode the merry-go-round the first year? _____

⸺ Plan ⸺

3. Which expression represents the money paid for rides the first year? _____

   a. 2 × 42,512   **b.** 2 × 92,000

4. How can you determine if the park earned or lost money in its first year?

   _____

   _____

5. Which estimate best represents the money earned or lost by the park? _____

   a. Loss: $90,000 – $85,000 = $5,000   **b.** Earned $90,000 + $5,000 = $95,000

6. How much money was paid for rides the first year? _____

7. What did the park earn or lose on this ride in its first year? _____

⸺ Look Back ⸺

8. How can you tell if your answer is reasonable? _____

   _____

   _____

SOLVE ANOTHER PROBLEM

It costs Ervin $15 to have his lawn mowed every two weeks for the 16 weeks of summer. He plans to buy a lawn mower for $175 and cut his own lawn this summer. How much money will he save or lose the first year? _____

Name _____

GPS PROBLEM 25, STUDENT PAGE 469

Antonio had scores of –1, –2, –1, –2, 0, 2, –1, –2, and –2 for nine holes on a miniature golf course. What was his mean score?

── Understand ──

1. What are you asked to find? _____

2. What is the definition of mean? _____

── Plan ──

3. Which method would you use to find the mean? _____

   a. Choose the score that appears most often.

   b. List all scores in order. Then find the middle number.

   c. Add the scores. Then divide by the number of scores.

── Solve ──

4. Add Antonio's scores. _____

5. How many holes did Antonio play? _____

6. Find the mean. _____

7. Write a sentence that answers the question.

   _____

   _____

── Look Back ──

8. Why do you think your answer is reasonable? _____

   _____

   _____

SOLVE ANOTHER PROBLEM

Heidi had scores of –1, 1, –2, 0, 2, 1, –2, –1, and 2 for nine holes on a miniature golf course. What was her mean score?

_____

_____

GPS PROBLEM 22, STUDENT PAGE 485

Certain types of animals always have the same number of legs, while others may have a varying number. Which of the quantities described are constants and which are variables?

a. The walking stick has 6 legs, as do all insects.

b. Sunstars, a type of starfish, can have up to 50 arms.

c. The cardinal has 2 legs, as do all other birds.

━━ Understand ━━

1. What types of quantities have values that cannot change? _____

2. What types of quantities have values that may change? _____

━━ Plan ━━

3. In parts a and c of the problem, what does the word *all* imply?

_____

4. In part b of the problem, what does the word *can* imply?

_____

━━ Solve ━━

5. Which of these quantities are constants, and which are variables?

   a. The number of legs an insect has. _____

   b. The number of arms a starfish has. _____

   c. The number of legs a bird has. _____

━━ Look Back ━━

6. How can you decide if your answers are reasonable? _____

_____

SOLVE ANOTHER PROBLEM

Is the number of legs on a cat a constant or a variable? _____

Name _____

GPS PROBLEM 13, STUDENT PAGE 489

The graphs show performances by three runners in the same race.
If the time scales are the same, which graph shows the winner's
performance? Explain.

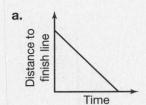

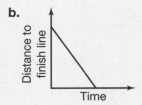

━━ **Understand** ━━

1. What relationship does each graph show?

_____

_____

━━ **Plan** ━━

2. Which of the graphs show that the runner reached the finish line? _____

3. What does the other graph show? _____

4. Would the winner take more time or less time than the other runners? _____

━━ **Solve** ━━

5. Which graph shows the winner's performance? Explain.

_____

_____

━━ **Look Back** ━━

6. How does the intersection of the graph and the *x-axis* help you
determine the winner?

_____

_____

_____

SOLVE ANOTHER PROBLEM

One of the runners was injured and quit the race. Which graph shows
his or her performance?

_____

GPS PROBLEM 34, STUDENT PAGE 494

The fifth term of an arithmetic sequence is 96. The difference between consecutive terms is 4. Find the first four terms.

▬ Understand ▬

1. What is an arithmetic sequence? _____

_____

2. How can you find consecutive terms in an arithmetic sequence? _____

   a. Multiply each previous term by the difference.

   b. Add the difference to each previous term.

3. What is the fifth term of the arithmetic sequence? _____

▬ Plan ▬

4. Which strategies can help you find the first four terms? _____

   a. Work Backward   **b.** Draw a Diagram   **c.** Either **a.** or **b.**

5. How much more is 96 than the amount of the fourth term? _____

6. How can you find the fourth term? _____

7. How can you find the third term, the second term, and the first term?

_____

_____

▬ Solve ▬

8. Find the first four terms of the sequence. _____

▬ Look Back ▬

9. How can you decide if your answers are reasonable? _____

_____

| SOLVE ANOTHER PROBLEM |

The fifth term of a geometric sequence is 567. Each term is three times the previous term. Find the first four terms in the sequence.

GPS | **PROBLEM 19, STUDENT PAGE 498**

As shown in the table, the cost of boarding a cat
in a kennel depends on the number of days it stays.

Days	2	4	6	7
Cost ($)	6	12	18	21

Which equation represents the relationship between cost and number of days?

(A) $C = d + 4$ **(B)** $C = \frac{d}{3}$ **(C)** $C = 3d$ **(D)** $C = 6d$

━ Understand ━

1. Which two quantities are related? _____

━ Plan ━

2. What operation will relate the two quantities?
   Is the change a constant one?

   _____

━ Solve ━

3. Describe the relationship between the number of days a cat is
   boarded and the cost.

   _____

4. Which equation represents this relationship? _____

━ Look Back ━

5. How could you use substitution to find the answer in another way?

   _____

   _____

   _____

| **SOLVE ANOTHER PROBLEM** |

As shown in the table, the cost of
feeding a dog depends on the
number of cans of dog food it eats.

Cans	2	4	5	7	10
Cost ($)	1.20	2.40	3.00	4.20	6.00

Which equation represents the relationship
between cans and cost? Let x = number of cans. _____

    (A) $C = 1.2x$ **(B)** $C = 2x$ **(C)** $C = 0.60x$ **(D)** $x = \frac{C}{2}$

Name _____

GPS PROBLEM 19, STUDENT PAGE 504

When an insect is active, its heart can beat at a rate of 140 beats per minute. When it is inactive and cold, its heart rate can slow to 1 beat per hour.

a. Write an equation to represent each of these rates.

b. Graph both equations on the same coordinate plane. Describe similarities and differences between these graphs. How can you tell by looking which graph represents the lesser rate?

━━ Understand ━━

1. How many heart beats are there when an insect is

a. active? _____   **b.** inactive? _____

━━ Plan ━━

2. How many heart beats are there per minute when an insect is inactive? _____

a. $\dfrac{60 \text{ beats}}{1 \text{ min}}$ **b.** $\dfrac{30 \text{ beats}}{60 \text{ min}}$ **c.** $\dfrac{\frac{1}{60} \text{ beat}}{1 \text{ min}}$

━━ Solve ━━

3. Use b for beats and m for minutes. Write the equation that represents the

a. active heartbeat. _____   **b.** inactive heartbeat. _____

4. Graph the equations.

5. Describe the similarities and differences.

_____

6. How can you tell by looking which graph represents the lesser rate?

_____

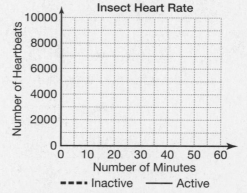

Insect Heart Rate

Number of Heartbeats / Number of Minutes

- - - - Inactive   ——— Active

━━ Look Back ━━

7. Do you have to graph the equations to tell which rate is the lesser one? Explain.

_____

SOLVE ANOTHER PROBLEM

An adult's heart can beat at a rate of 4800 times per hour. A new baby's heart can beat at a rate of 140 times per minute. Write an equation to represent each of these as $\frac{\text{beats}}{\text{hour}}$. Which represents the greater rate?

_____

GPS **PROBLEM 16, STUDENT PAGE 510**

Champ Cookies and Things is a business that began in a Washington, DC, school in 1987. Students bought the supplies, baked the cookies, and packaged and sold the cookies. Suppose the ingredients for one dozen cookies cost 35¢. Use a table to decide how many dozen cookies could be made for $7.70.

━━ Understand ━━

1. How much do the ingredients cost to make one dozen cookies? _____

2. Underline what you are asked to find.

━━ Plan ━━

3. Will you use negative numbers in your table? Explain.

_____

4. Complete the tables below to help you decide the answer to the question.

Number of dozen	1	2	3	4	5	10	12	14
Cost ($)		0.70	1.05					

Number of dozen	16	18	20	22	24	26	28	30
Cost ($)								

━━ Solve ━━

5. How many dozen cookies could be made for $7.70? _____

━━ Look Back ━━

6. How can you use division to check your answer?

_____

SOLVE ANOTHER PROBLEM

Suppose a package of three disks costs $1.95. Complete
the table to find how many packages can be bought for $9.75. _____

Package of disks	1	2	3	4	5	6	7
Cost ($)							

GPS PROBLEM 15, STUDENT PAGE 515

When you *lease* an automobile, you return it to the dealer after you have driven it for a certain amount of time. Suppose a car lease requires an initial payment of $1500 and payments of $300 at the end of each month. After how many months will the total cost of the lease be $4500? Use a graph to answer this question.

—— Understand ——

1. Write the amount of each payment.

   a. Initial payment _____   **b.** Monthly payment _____

2. Underline what you are asked to find.

—— Plan ——

3. Which equation shows the cost (*y*) of the lease after *x* months? _____

   a. $y = 1500x + 300$ **b.** $1500 = x + 300$ **c.** $y = 1500 + 300x$

4. Complete the table of values.

x	1	2	3	4
y				

5. What scale will you use for your graph?

   _____

   _____

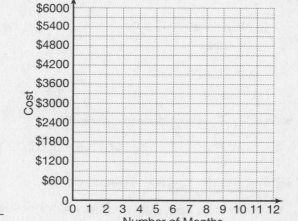

—— Solve ——

6. Plot and connect the points from the table in Item 4.

7. After how many months will the total cost of the lease be $4500? _____

—— Look Back ——

8. How can you check your answer? _____

   _____

SOLVE ANOTHER PROBLEM

The initial payment on a car lease is $1200. Each monthly payment is $250. Graph the data on the grid above to find how many months it will be until the cost of the lease is $2700. _____

Name _____

GPS **PROBLEM 34, STUDENT PAGE 520**

Answer each question for the integers –5 to 5. It may help to make a table.

a. When is $n = n^2$?   **b.** When is $n < n^2$?   **c.** When is $n > n^2$?

━━ Understand ━━

1. For each of the three questions, what
two values will you need to compare? _____

━━ Plan ━━

2. Suppose n is a negative integer. Will n^2 be positive or negative? Explain.

_____

3. Make a table of values for n from –5 to 5 and for each n^2.

n										
n^2										

━━ Solve ━━

4. Compare the n and n^2 values.

     a. When is $n = n^2$? _____

     b. When is $n < n^2$? _____

     c. When is $n > n^2$? _____

━━ Look Back ━━

5. What other strategy could you use to find the answer?

_____

SOLVE ANOTHER PROBLEM

Answer each question for the integers –3 to 3.

     a. When is $n = n^3$? _____

     b. When is $n < n^3$? _____

     c. When is $n > n^3$? _____

Name _____

GPS **PROBLEM 26, STUDENT PAGE 528**

The Dow Jones Industrial Average measures the prices of important stocks on the New York Stock Exchange. Suppose the Dow Jones average ends the week at 5602.10. The average lost 8.70 points on Monday, gained 37.70 on Tuesday, lost 11.25 on Wednesday, gained 24.90 on Thursday, and gained 27.15 on Friday. What was the Dow Jones average at the start of the week?

▬ Understand ▬

1. Where was the Dow Jones average at the end of the week? _____

2. How many changes were made during the week? _____

3. What are you asked to find?

_____

▬ Plan ▬

4. Which of the changes could be considered positive? Negative?

_____

5. Let *x* represent the Dow Jones average at the start of the week. Write an equation to show the change from the start of the week to the end of the week.

_____

▬ Solve ▬

6. Solve the equation you wrote in Item 5. What was the Dow Jones average at the start of the week? _____

▬ Look Back ▬

7. What other strategy could you use to find the answer?

_____

SOLVE ANOTHER PROBLEM

Suppose Jerome has an average of 87.2 in math. On the previous three tests, his average had gained 2.1 points, lost 3.4 points, and gained 1.5 points. What was his average before the last three tests? _____

© Scott Foresman Addison Wesley 7

GPS **PROBLEM 28, STUDENT PAGE 533**

Suppose the average low temperature for a 4-day period in Chicago, Illinois, is –8°F. After the next day, the 5-day average is –9°F. What was the low temperature for the fifth day? Explain your reasoning.

■■ Understand ■■■■

1. How do you find the average of several temperatures?

_____

2. If the average is –8°F, could some of the temperatures be

a. above –8°F? _____   **b.** below –8°F? _____

■■ Plan ■■■■■

3. If the average for a 4-day period is –8°F, what is the sum of the temperatures for a 4-day period? Explain.

_____

4. If the average for a 5-day period is –9°F, what is the sum of the temperatures for the 5-day period? Explain.

_____

5. What is the change in temperature between the 4-day period and the 5-day period? _____

■■ Solve ■■■■■

6. What is the low temperature for the fifth day? ___ _____

■■ Look Back ■■■■

7. How can you check to see if your answer is reasonable?

_____

_____

SOLVE ANOTHER PROBLEM

After 3 days, the average low temperature was –5°C.
After the next day, the 4-day average was –9°C.
What was the low temperature for the fourth day? _____

Name _____

 PROBLEM 24, STUDENT PAGE 538

Abraham Lincoln's famous speech, the Gettysburg Address, begins, "Four score and seven years ago." Lincoln was referring to the fact that the Declaration of Independence had been written 87 years earlier.

a. How many years are there in a score? Explain your answer.

b. If the Declaration of Independence was written in 1776, when did Lincoln give the Gettysburg Address?

━━ Understand ━━

1. Underline the information you will need to answer Question a.

2. What does Question b ask you to find?

_____

━━ Plan ━━

3. Which equation shows the relationship between "four score and seven" and 87? Let s represent score. _____

   a. $4s + 7 = 87$ **b.** $4s = 87 + 7$ **c.** $4s - 7 = 87$

4. Which operation would you perform to find the year the Gettysburg Address is given? _____

   a. Subtract 87 from 1776.   **b.** Add 87 to 1776.

━━ Solve ━━

5. To find how many years are in a score, solve the equation chosen in Item 3. Explain how you found your answer.

_____

6. When did Lincoln give the Gettysburg Address? _____

━━ Look Back ━━

7. How can you estimate to see if your answer to part b is reasonable?

_____

SOLVE ANOTHER PROBLEM

Suppose "five glyphs and 3 years ago" means something happened 68 years ago. How long is a glyph? _____

GPS PROBLEM 10, STUDENT PAGE 542

Suppose it costs 25¢ for the first minute of a long distance phone call and 15¢ for each additional minute. The cost of a phone call can then be expressed by the formula $c = 0.25 + 0.15(m - 1)$, where c is the total cost in dollars and m is the number of minutes.

a. For $1.75, how long can you talk?

b. What is the cost of a call that lasts 1 hour 15 minutes?

━━ Understand ━━

1. Underline the formula showing how to find the cost of a phone call.

2. What do c and m represent in the formula? _____

━━ Plan ━━

3. You can substitute $1.75 (from part a) for which variable in the formula? _____

4. Write the formula, substituting 1.75 for the chosen variable.

_____

5. Look at part b. How many minutes are in 1 hour 15 minutes? _____

6. Write the formula, substituting 75 for m. _____

━━ Solve ━━

7. How long can you talk for $1.75? Solve the formula in Item 4. _____

8. What is the cost of a call that lasts 1 hour 15 minutes?
Solve the formula in Item 6.   _____

━━ Look Back ━━

9. What other strategy might you use to help you solve this problem?

_____

| SOLVE ANOTHER PROBLEM |

A car rental is $25 for the day and 22¢ per mile.

a. For $91, how many miles could you drive? _____

b. What is the cost to rent the car for one day and drive 225 miles? _____

Name _____

GPS **PROBLEM 13, STUDENT PAGE 556**

How many faces, edges, and vertices does a square pyramid have?

A. 4 faces, 8 edges, 6 vertices
B. 4 faces, 6 edges, 4 vertices
C. 5 faces, 8 edges, 5 vertices
D. 5 faces, 9 edges, 6 vertices

━━ Understand ━━

1. What figure is the base of a square pyramid? _____

2. Does a pyramid have two congruent parallel bases or one base opposite a point?

_____

━━ Plan ━━

3. Draw a square pyramid. Label the vertices *A, B, C,* and so on.

4. List the vertices. _____

5. List the edges. _____

6. List the faces. _____

━━ Solve ━━

7. Use your answers to Items 4–6 to tell how many of each there are in a square pyramid.

   a. Vertices _____ **b.** Edges _____ **c.** Faces _____

8. Which choice is the correct answer. _____

━━ Look Back ━━

9. How did making an organized list help you know that you counted all the edges? _____

_____

SOLVE ANOTHER PROBLEM

How many faces, edges, and vertices does a hexagonal prism have?

_____

Name _____

GPS **PROBLEM 9, STUDENT PAGE 562**

Sketch front, top, and side
views of this object.

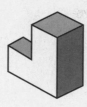

━━ Understand ━━

1. Which views are you asked to sketch? _____

━━ Plan ━━

2. Label the front, top, and side views on the drawing above.

3. Which of the angles below will be in your sketch? _____

    a. Acute   **b.** Obtuse   **c.** Right

4. Which of these views will you use in your sketch? _____

    a.   **b.**   **c.**   **d.**

━━ Solve ━━

5. Sketch each view.

    a. Front   **b.** Top   **c.** Side

━━ Look Back ━━

6. How can you check that your
views are accurately sketched? _____

_____

SOLVE ANOTHER PROBLEM

Sketch the front, top, and side views of this object.

    a. Front   **b.** Top   **c.** Side

Name _____

GPS PROBLEM 9, STUDENT PAGE 565

You need to paint the outside of the house shown. A gallon of paint covers between 300 and 400 square feet. How many gallons will you need to buy? (Ignore the areas of windows and doors, and do not paint the roof!)

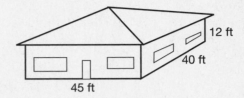

12 ft
40 ft
45 ft

—— Understand ——

1. How many sides must be painted? _____

2. How many square feet does one gallon of paint cover? Give a range. _____

3. What are the dimensions of the front (and back) of the house? _____

4. What are the dimensions of each of the other two sides of the house? _____

—— Plan ——

5. What formula will you use to find the area of each side? _____

6. What is the area of each side of the house?

   a. Front _____   **b.** Back _____

   c. Right side _____   **d.** Left side _____

—— Solve ——

7. What is the total area of the house? _____

8. Divide the total area by 300. _____   By 400. _____

9. How many gallons of paint will you need to buy to be certain that you will not run out? _____

—— Look Back ——

10. Did you over or under estimate? Why? _____

_____

| SOLVE ANOTHER PROBLEM |

A gallery is 30 feet long and 24 feet wide. The walls are 10 feet high. Assume that a gallon of paint will cover 300 to 400 square feet. How many gallons of paint will you need to buy to be sure you have enough to paint all four walls of the gallery? _____

Name _____

GPS PROBLEM 8, STUDENT PAGE 569

The two boxes of sugar are the
same price. Which one is the
better buy? Explain your answer.

A.
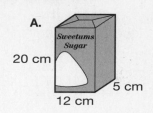
20 cm
12 cm
5 cm
Sweetums Sugar

B.
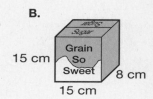
15 cm
15 cm
8 cm
Grain So Sweet

▬ Understand ▬

1. Assume that the size of the box relates to the amount
   it holds. How will you find the amount each box holds? _____

2. What shape are the boxes? _____

3. What are the dimensions in cm of each box?

   a. Sweetums Sugar _____ **b.** Grain So Sweet _____

▬ Plan ▬

4. What formula will you use to find the volume of each box? _____

5. What is the area of the base of each package?

   a. Sweetums Sugar _____ **b.** Grain So Sweet _____

▬ Solve ▬

6. What is the volume of the package of each product?

   a. Sweetums Sugar? _____ **b.** Grain So Sweet? _____

7. Which is the better buy? Explain. _____

_____

▬ Look Back ▬

8. Does the sugar necessarily fill the volume of the package?
   What else might you consider in your decision?

_____

SOLVE ANOTHER PROBLEM

Two white porcelain boxes are the same price. Box A has
a 3 cm by 2 cm rectangular base and a height of 4 cm.
Box B has a 3 cm by 4 cm rectangular base and a height
of 3 cm. Which is the better buy?

_____

Name _____

 PROBLEM 11, STUDENT PAGE 577

In the game of Disc Golf, a flying disc is thrown at a series of far-off targets. Analyze the score data, and make a circle graph to show your results.

Hole Number	1	2	3	4	5	6	7	8	9	10	11	12	13	14	15	16	17	18
Score	3	4	4	5	4	4	4	4	4	5	4	4	4	3	3	4	3	3

— Understand —

1. What type of graph are you asked to make? _____

— Plan —

2. How many holes had each score?

   a. 3 _____ **b.** 4 _____ **c.** 5 _____

3. Find what percent each score was of the 18 holes. Round your answer to the nearest tenth of a percent.

   a. 3 _____ **b.** 4 _____ **c.** 5 _____

4. Multiply each percent by 360° to find the central angle needed to graph each score. Round your answer to the nearest whole degree.

   a. 3 _____ **b.** 4 _____ **c.** 5 _____

— Solve —

5. Make a circle graph.

— Look Back —

6. How can you check your calculations without recalculating?

   _____

   _____

SOLVE ANOTHER PROBLEM

A dart game has five rings worth 1, 2, 3, 4, and 5 points each. The scores for ten dart throws are shown below. Analyze the data and make a circle graph to show your results.

Dart Throw	1	2	3	4	5	6	7	8	9	10
Score	2	2	4	4	1	3	3	4	3	5

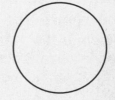

GPS PROBLEM 22, STUDENT PAGE 581

The running track is made up of two
half-circles at either end of a rectangle.
Find the approximate distance around
the track.

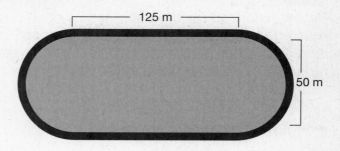

125 m

50 m

━ Understand ━

1. What is the length of each straight portion of the track? _____

2. What shape makes up each end of the track? _____

━ Plan ━

3. How will you find the total length of the straight sections? _____

4. If the two half-circles were joined to make one shape,
   they would be a circle. What is the diameter of the circle? _____

5. What is another name for the distance around a circle? _____

6. What formula will you use to find the length
   of the track made up by the two half-circles? _____

━ Solve ━

7. What is the total length of the straight portions of the track? _____

8. What is the total length of the two
   half-circles of the track? Use 3.14 for π.

9. What is the total distance around the track?

━ Look Back ━

10. Why was it easier to use 3.14 than $\frac{22}{7}$ for π? _____

_____

SOLVE ANOTHER PROBLEM

The midget car track is made up of two
half-circles at either end of a rectangle. Find
the approximate distance around the track.

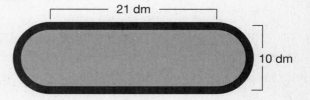

21 dm

10 dm

GPS **PROBLEM 23, STUDENT PAGE 586**

Native American children sometimes used hoops to practice their aim. A screen was put in the center of the hoop. Then the hoop was rolled along the ground between two lines of players, who hurled darts at the rapidly moving target. If a target hoop had a circumference of 60 in., what was its area?

Understand

1. What figure is the hoop? _____

2. What are you asked to find? _____

3. What information are you given? _____

Plan

4. What is the formula for finding the area of a circle? _____

5. There are two formulas for finding circumference. What are they? _____

6. Select a circumference formula. Solve for the unknown variable using 3.14 for π. Round your answer to the nearest hundredth.

_____

Solve

7. Use your answer to Item 6 to write an equation to find the area of the hoop. Round your answer to the nearest whole number.

_____

8. What is the area of the hoop? _____

Look Back

9. How could you have found the area if you had used the other circumference formula? _____

_____

_____

SOLVE ANOTHER PROBLEM

If the area of the hoop was 50.24 m², what was its circumference? _____

© Scott Foresman Addison Wesley 7

Name _____

GPS | PROBLEM 14, STUDENT PAGE 591

A cylinder with a radius of 5 cm has a surface area of 345.4 cm^2.
What is its height?

—— Understand ——

1. Underline the measurements of the cylinder you are given.

2. What are you asked to find? _____

—— Plan ——

3. Draw a net of the cylinder.

4. What is the formula for
   finding the area of *one* base?

   _____

5. Once you know the surface area and
   the area of *both* bases, which operation
   will you use to find the area of the rectangle?

   _____

6. Which measure of a circle is
   equal to the length of the rectangle? _____

7. What is the formula for finding the
   length of the rectangular surface? _____

8. Once you know the area of the rectangle and the
   length, which operation will you use to find the width? _____

—— Solve ——

9. What is the area of *one* base? _____ Of *both* bases? _____

10. What is the area of the rectangle? _____ The length? _____

11. The width of the rectangle is the height of
    the cylinder. What is the height of the cylinder? _____

—— Look Back ——

12. Did drawing a net help you find the answer? Explain. _____

_____

| SOLVE ANOTHER PROBLEM |

A cylinder with a radius of 3 in. has a
surface area of 244.92 in^2. What is its height? _____

GPS PROBLEM 10, STUDENT PAGE 595

A typical soft drink can has a height of about 4.8 in. and a diameter of about 2.5 in. A case that holds 12 cans is a rectangular prism about 5 in. tall, 11 in. long, and 7.6 in. wide.

a. What is the total volume of the 12 cans?

b. What is the volume of the case?

c. What percent of the space in the case is taken up by the cans?

━━ Understand ━━

1. Circle the measures of a cylindrical soft drink can.

2. Underline the dimensions of the case.

━━ Plan ━━

3. What formula will you use to find the volume of one can? _____

4. Which operation will you use to find the volume of 12 cans? _____

5. What formula will you use to find the volume of the case? _____

6. How would you find the percent of space taken up by cans? _____

    a. $\dfrac{\text{Volume of 12 cans}}{\text{Volume of case}} = \dfrac{x}{100}$ **b.** $\dfrac{\text{Volume of 1 can}}{\text{Volume of 12 cans}} = \dfrac{x}{100}$

━━ Solve ━━

7. What is the total volume of one can? _____ Of 12 cans? _____

8. What is the volume of the case? _____

9. What percent of the space in the case is taken up by the 12 cans? _____

━━ Look Back ━━

10. What is another way to find the percent? _____

_____

| SOLVE ANOTHER PROBLEM |

A cylindrical tub of popcorn has a radius of 2.5 in. and a height of 9 in. The case it is packed in is a rectangular prism with a base measuring 5.4 in. on each side and a height of 9.4 in. Round answers to nearest whole number.

a. What is the volume of the popcorn tub? _____ Of the case? _____

b. What percent of the space in the case is taken up by the popcorn tub?

Name _____

A transformation of △ABC moves A(2, −3) to D (0, −2), B(1, 4) to E(−1, 5), and C(−2, 1) to F(−4, 2). Is △DEF a translation of △ABC? If so, what is the rule for the translation? If not, why not?

— Understand —

1. Does each point in a translation move in the same or in a different direction? _____

2. Does each point in a translation move the same or a different number of units in each direction? _____

3. Write the coordinates for each point.

   a. Point A _____   **b.** Point B _____   **c.** Point C _____

   d. Point D _____   **e.** Point E _____   **f.** Point F _____

— Plan —

4. Use the words left or right and up or down to describe the movement between each point.

   a. Point A to Point D _____   **b.** Point B to Point E _____

   c. Point C to Point F _____

5. Which movements are written as addition when you write a rule? _____

— Solve —

6. If the movement is a translation, write the rule using (x, y) notation. If it is not a translation, explain.

   _____

— Look Back —

7. What other strategy could you use to find the answer?

   _____

A transformation of △GHI moves G(−2, −1) to J (0, 4), H(5, −1) to K(0, −2), and I(2, 3) to L(7, −2) Is △JKL a translation of △GHI? If so, what is the rule for the translation? If not, why not? _____

_____

GPS **PROBLEM 8, STUDENT PAGE 609**

Draw the reflection of △JKL across the x-axis.
Give the coordinates of the reflection's vertices.

── Understand ──

1. Which axis will you draw
   the reflection across? _____

2. Will the x-coordinate or the
   y-coordinate change? _____

3. Write the coordinates for each point.

   a. Point J _____   **b.** Point K _____   **c.** Point L _____

── Plan ──

4. How many units above the x-axis is each point?

   a. Point J _____   **b.** Point K _____   **c.** Point L _____

5. How many units left of the y-axis is each point?

   a. Point J _____   **b.** Point K _____   **c.** Point L _____

── Solve ──

6. Draw the reflection of △JKL on the coordinate plane at the top
   of the page. Label the points J′, K′, and L′.

7. Write each coordinate.

   a. Point J′ _____   **b.** Point K′ _____   **c.** Point L′ _____

── Look Back ──

8. What is the line of symmetry in your reflection? _____

SOLVE ANOTHER PROBLEM

Draw the reflection of △STU across the y-axis.
Give the coordinates of the reflection's vertices.

a. Point S′ _____

b. Point T′ _____

c. Point U′ _____

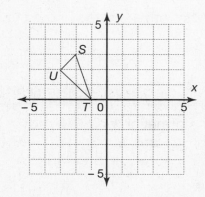

Name _____

GPS PROBLEM 15, STUDENT PAGE 614

Decide whether each of these regular polygons has rotational symmetry. If it does, name all clockwise fractional turns that rotate the figure onto itself.

a. Equilateral triangle   **b.** Square

c. Regular pentagon   **d.** Regular hexagon

e. What pattern of rotational symmetry is there for regular polygons?

━━ Understand ━━

1. What do equilateral triangles, squares, and other regular polygons have in common? _____

_____

━━ Plan ━━

2. Sketch each
regular polygon.

Equilateral triangle   Square   Pentagon   Hexagon

━━ Solve ━━

3. Imagine each polygon rotating around its center. Then complete the table. Write *yes* or *no* to describe the rotational symmetry.

	Triangle	Square	Pentagon	Hexagon
Rotational symmetry				
Fractional turns				

4. What pattern of rotational symmetry is there for regular polygons?

_____

━━ Look Back ━━

5. How could you prove your answer to someone who doesn't understand rotational symmetry? _____

SOLVE ANOTHER PROBLEM

What clockwise fractional turns would rotate a regular octagon onto itself? Explain.

_____

_____

GPS **PROBLEM 8, STUDENT PAGE 629**

The Out To Lunch restaurant chain offers customers their choice of one
kind of soup and one sandwich. On Monday, the soups are chicken
noodle and tomato, and the sandwiches are roast beef, turkey, and
veggie. How many different lunches can be selected, and what are they?

━ Understand ━

1. Underline what you are asked to find.

━ Plan ━

2. Which method can you use to find the number of possible outcomes? _____

   a. Organized list   **b.** Tree diagram   **c.** Counting Principle   **d.** Any of them

━ Solve ━

3. Use one of the counting methods to show each possible outcome.

4. How many different lunches can be selected? _____

━ Look Back ━

5. How can you use the Counting Principle to make sure you have
listed all the possible outcomes?

_____

_____

SOLVE ANOTHER PROBLEM

On Tuesday, the restaurant offers these choices. Soups are barley,
corn chowder, and potato. Sandwiches are ham, veggie, salami,
and turkey. How many different lunches can be selected and what
are they?

_____

Name _____

GPS PROBLEM 13, STUDENT PAGE 635

Complete the table below for the equation $y = x!$. Then graph your results. What do you notice about the growth of factorial products?

x	2	3	4	5	6	7	8	9	10
$y = x!$									

── Understand ──

1. What are you asked to do? _____

── Plan ──

2. What do you need to do to find $x!$? _____
   a. Add all the whole numbers from x to 1.
   b. Multiply all the whole numbers from x to 1.

── Solve ──

3. Write each factorial product in the table.

4. Graph your results on the grid at the right.

5. What do you notice about the growth of factorial products?

_____

_____

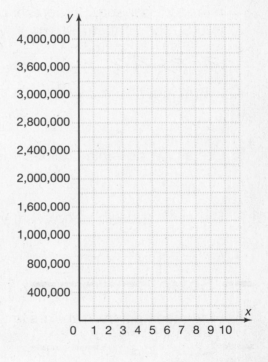

── Look Back ──

6. What pattern in the table can you use to check the factorial products?

_____

_____

SOLVE ANOTHER PROBLEM

On the grid above, graph $y = (x - 1)!$. Use x values 2 through 11. How does your graph compare to the one in the problem above?

_____

GPS PROBLEM 14, STUDENT PAGE 640

Suppose you can choose 1, 2, 3, *or* 4 of the following fruits for a fruit shake: Banana, blueberry, pineapple, and strawberry. How many different shakes are possible?

— Understand —

1. How many fruits can you use in your choice of shake? *I can choose 4 flavors*

2. Name the fruits from which you can choose.

   Ba, Bl, P, S

— Plan —

3. List all the possible choices if you choose only 1 fruit. Let Ba represent banana, Bl represent blueberry, P represent pineapple, and S represent strawberry in your lists.

   Ba, Bl, P

4. List all the possible choices if you choose 2 fruits.

   _____

5. List all the possible choices if you choose 3 fruits.

   _____

6. List all the possible choices if you choose 4 fruits.

   _____

— Solve —

7. How many different shakes are possible? _____

— Look Back —

8. How can you use a tree diagram to check your answer?

   _____

| SOLVE ANOTHER PROBLEM |

Suppose you can choose 1, 2, *or* 3 toppings for your pizza: extra cheese, sausage, or pepperoni. How many different pizzas are possible?

_____

Name _____

GPS **PROBLEM 21, STUDENT PAGE 648**

This spinner is used in a game where one team is yellow and one is green. If the spinner lands on yellow, the yellow team gets 6 points. If it lands on green, the green team gets 2 points. The first team to reach 6000 points wins. Is this a fair game? Justify your answer.

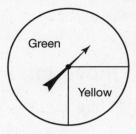

■ Understand ■

1. Which color is the spinner more likely to land on? Explain.

_____

■ Plan ■

2. Suppose the circle were divided into fourths. How many fourths would be

   a. green? _____   **b.** yellow? _____

3. How many times larger than the
   yellow section is the green section? _____

4. How should the number of points for spinning yellow compare to the number of points for spinning green?

_____

■ Solve ■

5. If the spinner lands on yellow, the yellow team scores 6 points. If it lands on green, the green team scores 2 points. Is this a fair game? Justify your answer.

_____

_____

■ Look Back ■

6. Write the odds of winning and the number of
   points as two ratios. Do they form a proportion? _____

SOLVE ANOTHER PROBLEM

If the spinner lands on red, the red team scores 8 points. It it lands on blue, the blue team scores 2 points. Is this a fair game? Justify your answer.

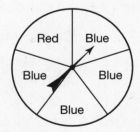

_____

Name _____

GPS PROBLEM 20, STUDENT PAGE 653

Which of these odds means the same thing as a probability of 25%?

(A) 1:5   **(B)** 1:4   **(C)** 1:3   **(D)** 1:2

▬ Understand ▬

1. What fraction means the same as 25%? _____

2. What does a probability of 25% mean?

   _____

3. Which describes how to find the probability of an event? _____

   a. number of ways the event can happen:number of ways it cannot happen
   b. number of ways the event can happen:number of possible outcomes

▬ Plan ▬

4. What does the first number mean when given odds of an event?

   _____

5. What does the second number mean when given odds of an event?

   _____

6. When given the odds of an event, how can you find the number of possible outcomes? _____

   a. Add both numbers.   **b.** Multiply both numbers.

7. Write each odds as a probability the event will happen.

   a. 1:5 _____   **b.** 1:4 _____   **c.** 1:3 _____   **d.** 1:2 _____

▬ Solve ▬

8. Which is the correct choice? _____

▬ Look Back ▬

9. How can you determine probability when given the odds?

   _____

SOLVE ANOTHER PROBLEM

Which of these odds means the same thing as a probability of 10%? _____

   (A) 1:5   **(B)** 1:11   **(C)** 1:10   **(D)** 1:9

Name _____

GPS | **PROBLEM 20, STUDENT PAGE 658**

In a coin toss game you earn points for landing on the shaded figures. Assume coins land randomly in the large square. What is the probability that a coin lands on the right triangle?

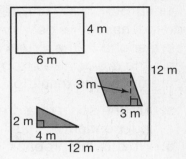

—— Understand ——

1. Underline what you are asked to find.

2. Which ratio will you use to find the probability? _____

    a. Area of right triangle : area of square
    b. Area of right triangle : perimeter of square

—— Plan ——

3. Which formula will you use to find the area of the large square? _____

    a. $A = \frac{1}{2}bh$ **b.** $A = l \times w$ **c.** $A = \pi r^2$

4. Which formula will you use to find the area of the right triangle? _____

    a. $A = \frac{1}{2}bh$ **b.** $A = l \times w$ **c.** $A = \pi r^2$

—— Solve ——

5. Find the area of the large square. _____

6. Find the area of the right triangle. _____

7. Find the probability that a coin lands on the right triangle. _____

—— Look Back ——

8. What strategy could help you decide if your answer is reasonable?

_____

_____

| **SOLVE ANOTHER PROBLEM** |

Coins are randomly tossed on the rectangle at the right. Find the probability that a coin lands on the shaded parallelogram. Assume coins land randomly in the large square.

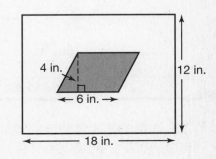

_____

Name _____

GPS PROBLEM 8, STUDENT PAGE 662

During Hanukkah, children play with a *dreidel*. The dreidel has four sides, with the Hebrew letters that correspond to the letters N, G, S, and H. The children spin the dreidel like a top, and the letter that comes up determines the result for each turn.

   a. Are the spins of a dreidel dependent or independent events?

   b. What is the probability of spinning 2 Hs in a row?

— Understand —

1. How many sides does a dreidel have? _____

2. Which letters correspond to the Hebrew letters on the sides of the dreidel? _____

— Plan —

3. Will the result of the first spin change the possible outcome for the second spin? _____

4. How many possible outcomes are there for one spin? _____

5. How many ways can you spin an H? _____

6. What is the probability of spinning an H on the

   a. first spin? _____   **b.** second spin? _____

7. How can you find the probability of two events? _____

— Solve —

8. Are the spins of a dreidel dependent or independent events? _____

9. What is the probability of spinning 2 Hs in a row? _____

— Look Back —

10. How did you decide whether or not the events were dependent or independent?

_____

_____

SOLVE ANOTHER PROBLEM

What is the probability of spinning a G, then spinning an A, on the dreidel? _____